The forces of Fingall and Rodger attack the keep of Calhoun.
Harold swims ashore and is made prisoner.
Bold Rodger man-aged to reach Fin-galls coast about dusk."
LANCASHIRE
Harold meets the Viking fleet
Galley
The Roman trans-ports are captured
SCILLY IS.
LANDS END
C. V. FARROW

TRADER HORN

Volume Two

Aloysius Horn

"HAROLD THE WEBBED
OR THE YOUNG VYKINGS":

BEING VOLUME TWO OF
THE LIFE AND WORKS OF

TRADER HORN

...*the works written by* ALFRED ALOYSIUS HORN
*at the age of seventy-three, & the life with
such of his philosophy as is the gift of
age and experience, taken down
and here edited by*

ETHELREDA LEWIS

With a foreword by WILLIAM McFEE

THE LITERARY GUILD OF AMERICA, INC.
NEW YORK *MCMXXVIII*

Printed in U. S. A.

TRADER HORN

VOLUME TWO

FOREWORD

ABOUT a year ago a telegram came to this quiet Connecticut village from the Herald Tribune in New York asking me to review an African book called *Trader Horn* which seemed "interesting." No author's name was mentioned. Irita Van Doren's telegram seemed charged with excitement, as though she had looked into this new book and had seen something in it that was destined to give the reviewer a run for his money. Literary editors can do that sometimes, but not often. Most of them keep such books for their own columns and send out the incombustible débris on their desks to their long-suffering minions.

My second thoughts, however, which beset me as I turned over the pages of *Trader Horn* for the first time, were of another order. Memories began to stir. Hullo! I muttered, one of those old-timers has made good his threat and done a book after all. Memories began to stir. As I looked at the picture of the old trader which formed the frontispiece and glanced sideways at the first words of the story about St. Edward's College I began to see things. The map which formed the endpapers brought all those vibrating images into focus. And I was back on the Niger again.

But even then I was not willing to believe that anything had really happened. I have been taken in too often by the books of old-timers. They are a weariful race! They always fill their books with the wrong memories. Nine out of ten of them cannot tell their stories. They are for the most part like those red-nosed and tedious old adventurers I have encountered in many years at sea who promise you a story and when they have drunk up most of the whisky try to borrow five shillings. More than once I have paid my halfcrown for a fine large book (published at seven and sixpence net) with a resounding title like *The Log of a Rolling Stone* or *A Beachcomber's Romance* only to discover that I have spent my money in vain. Put not your trust in publishers' remainders!

The first note of encouragement came to me in the dedicatory inscription of Mrs. Lewis to her old Trader. He has got some one to write it for him, I reflected; I am not so badly off after all.

The reader must understand that a reviewer does not start on a book like one of the purchasing public. For instance, the reviewer doesn't buy the book; he is paid to read it; and he is therefore absolved from sternly demanding his money's worth. He looks for pitfalls and snares. Publishers are aggressive sometimes, and it is necessary for reviewers to maintain an attitude of sour unbelief to balance the almost incredible optimism of the jacket-blurb writers. If there be neither publisher's name nor blurb, as in the case of my copy of *Trader Horn,* the reviewer immediately suspects some new merchandising device. Later on, when he has time, he opens the book again cautiously and begins to read.

And all the time occupied in these various employments I was going over my memories of the Niger River run in the African Royal Mail out of Liverpool. Or, to put it more accurately, I was trying to revive the tales I had heard of the early days while I myself was working on a ship up the Niger bends during the first few months of the war. I was a newcomer into the company, part of a temporary influx caused by the war. My seniors were old West African hands. They were indissolubly linked in their lives, their fortunes and their memories with the company. For all I know, if they have survived hostilities, those men are still steaming up the innumerable streams of the Niger Delta, still anchoring below the red bluff of Old Calabar, still voyaging into Duala behind Fernando Po, still rolling in the oily swell of the Ivory Coast off Cape Coast Castle. No doubt they still tell new hands the old story of the West African chief, wealthy in palm oil and ivory, who was taken to Liverpool and who returned to his tribe telling of an island he had visited "where the natives were friendly."

And out of that time of never-ending toil and equatorial heat I can remember stories of the traders who preceded the huge capitalistic combine for which we were working. "Hatton and Cookson" was one firm, and that name, suddenly encountered in *Trader Horn,* brought before me my old chief on that run. He, however, was a comparatively young man; not more than fifty. His authority was always another chief, immeasurably older. Indeed, he had been nearly fifty years with the company. My oiler, it turned out, had been with him. Even the oilers in those ships carried on year after year. This oiler of mine, as we stood by the levers working the eight-thousand-ton *Salaga* up the river to some jumble of sheds where a dozen barrels of palm oil awaited us, would allude to this unusual old chap with a mixture of respect and alarm. Old Goodyard! That was no more his name than Trader Horn is the name of the author of this book, but it will serve. It will serve because old Goodyard is but a symbol here of another phase of the Earlies. His image came to me through the misty medium of a man's illiterate memory. He came to me as an old, old man with a white, tobacco-stained beard wandering like a ghost through that West African ship at night bearing a portable electric lamp, like some forlorn and disillusioned Diogenes suffering from insomnia. He came to me as an old, old man whose thoughts were in the past, whose prestige was so great with the company that he had an extra engineer on board, whose cabin was full of dreadful-looking idols and animals' heads, so that it was "enough to frighten a Christian." He would come shuffling along in the dead of night, a pipe in his mouth, his pale eyes fixed on invisible things. "Gave you a fair start, he did, sir," said my oiler, a Lancashire man himself.

They were all Lancashire men in that ship and you could never get away from it. Those who think the Scot is a clansman should sail out of Liverpool in one of those West African ships and try to make a dint in the pride, in the self-sufficiency, in the unbelievable racial poise of Lancashire men. You would think the Wars of the Roses were still raging! Even Francis Thompson had a touch of it when he spoke of "the Southern men" in his poetry. They are a sort of little England within England, with strong prejudices and impregnable silences, and occasional dark suspicions of your motives when you pry into their lives. Try to get below the surface with those folk who live round Hornby Castle, and watch the slow drawing together of their spirits, the slightly blank look on their faces when you make a joke at the expense of Lancashire. Their minds have a sort of tough cartilaginous texture which is one of the excellent ingredients of the English character.

Yes, they were all Lancashire men, and so was old Goodyard, the chief engineer who had been nearly fifty years in the employ, who had made a marvelous collection of idols and ju-jus, of weapons and paddles and household implements. For years he had been at this, learning the lore of the tribes, gaining the confidence of the chiefs whose oil and nuts form the precious freight those ships take home to Liverpool. You can see those collections if you visit the city. "Sir Alfred, he gave special instructions old Mr. Goodyard was to be allowed ashore wherever we touched. 'Is cabin was full of 'earthen images. 'E 'ad a 'uman 'ead. . . . Gave me a turn all right. . . ."

And as time passed the picture formed in my mind

of a patriarchal figure in soiled uniform moving slowly along to the gangway to go ashore with some huge black chieftain, his breast covered with a long white beard, a blackened briar pipe protruding from his nicotine-stained moustache. Old Goodyard! Oldest chief in the company. Friend of Sir Alfred. One of the survivals of the days before Elder Dempster's and Woermann's, British and German, crowded out the early traders and brought Big Business to West Africa.

And so exactly like this picture in my mind was the portrait of Trader Horn that I was in a state of high excitement when I began to read. The names on the map evoked memories, the strange childish names which for me meant clearings in the forest with some sheds, some houses and a jetty, with perhaps a narrow-gauge track. They meant interminable reaches of mangrove swamps, great stretches of shining water suddenly blocked by unexpected islands and lonely white buoys marking the last new shift of the ever-shifting channel. I would put the book down and think of it. This talkative old chap who had been to St. Edwards College must have been one of the pioneers. I turned to the preface and realized even as a hardened reviewer that Mr. Galsworthy had made no mistake. He had made, on the other hand, one of those discoveries that only come once in a lifetime.

There is no need to go into detail concerning the excitement which came to so many of us in that first reading of *Trader Horn*. The book, once afloat, made a wash that is still rolling across the world. What is of more interest at this time is the attitude of the press.

There is no doubt that Trader Horn and his book, as arranged by Ethelreda Lewis, caught some of the critics in a cantankerous mood. Some praised it, it is true; but certain majestic organs of public opinion turned their heaviest guns to bear. They suspected a trick at once. They approached the book not as literary critics but as Scotland Yard men. And it is worth while noting here that their principal reason for doubting the authenticity of Trader Horn's African adventures was his avowed familiarity with the literary taste of the United States! They were so completely convinced of the African experiences, in fact, that they were unable to conceive the author of them in any other circumstances. They were so cockneyfied in their outlook that such a contingency never occurred to them. It would have been as reasonable to doubt Sir H. M. Stanley's story of Darkest Africa because he had at one time been a resident of New Orleans.

Perhaps the most crushing criticism of all appeared in the Manchester Guardian, that palladium of English Liberalism. "We have been amused," said the Guardian with devastating irony. *Trader Horn* was methodically butchered to make a Manchester holiday. And the really amusing feature of the situation lay in the triviality of the criticisms themselves. The reviewer in his preoccupation with superficial flaws missed the whole thing. It was as though a man, reading the autobiography of Benvenuto Cellini for the first time, became extremely amused over Cellini's preposterous tales of visions and miracles and ignored the terrific vitality of the book. It was as though a man picking up Hakluyt's account of some early voyaging should dismiss it as an amusing compilation because Hakluyt took the story down from some ear-ringed and voluble seaman who was shaky about dates and who ran one episode into another. It was as though a reader of Shakespeare's *Tempest* became amused at the author's improbable characters Ariel and Caliban.

Even the United States, whose tastes in literature Trader Horn seemed to know with such uncanny accuracy, produced some stupendously solemn reviews. Critics of high integrity gave as their measured opinion the curious verdict that *Trader Horn* was a clever swindle. I myself have always felt a tinge of regret that these gentlemen did not deign to particularize, since it was distasteful to me to be associated in any way with an attempt to deceive the public. It seemed to reflect even more emphatically upon Mr. John Galsworthy, who had happened to be in South Africa at the moment when Mrs. Ethelreda Lewis received back the manuscript of *Trader Horn* from a London publisher. This rejection, based upon the publisher's conviction that the book "was not of sufficient public interest to warrant acceptance," had depressed Mrs. Lewis and she seized the chance to obtain an unbiased judgment. The eminent English novelist, as might be expected, needed a remarkably short time to make up his mind. He wired, and took the train for Johannesburg. He was already writing his brief but vigorous introduction. He arrived, he saw Trader Horn, and came to the conclusion that the fantastic narrative was the old man's unaided work. He savored—as what writer would not?—the amazingly naïve and disconcertingly shrewd conversational comments which Trader Horn made upon the business of writing. Even more was he enraptured with the powerful and curiously original phrases the old man struck out. This time the book found a publisher. Its reception in America need not detain us. In form, in the rapidity with which it made its way and in ultimate sales it seems likely to be one of the most remarkable discoveries of a decade.

The difficulty the adverse critics seem to have encountered is simply this, that while there are innumerable talkative old adventurers in the world very few indeed possess the peculiar quality of our Mr. Horn. We who enjoy his work are not claiming for him the position of a great novelist. His stories, as works of fiction, are perhaps no more than those of Harold Bell Wright or the late James Oliver Curwood. They are the crude and shaky contraptions of an elderly amateur. When reading, our pleasure is derived from seeing the story-telling faculty, reduced to its simplest components, operating in full view of the reader. We are taken, as never before, into a sort of airtight, soundproof cubicle where no hint of the real world of to-day can reach us, and we can look through a small window at an elderly Victorian busily cutting out little wooden figures of men and women and wild animals, painting them in the bright colors of his fancy and pulling strings which cause them to perform all the conventional movements of the old out-of-date romances. As Mrs. Lewis says, Mr. Horn has preserved his illusions by not reading, and although the London Times sarcastically inquires how a man so familiar with American taste in books and so forth can be said to have given up reading, the statement is fundamentally true. Mr. Horn in his recent years has read very little, not because he lacked the intrinsic intelligence but because he was living very much in the past. People who reach the later stretches of human life without having succeeded in winning a competence do often live in the past. They go through the motions of everyday existence, even to reading the newspaper and seeking a livelihood, but their minds are elsewhere. It is a strange thing to me that men, clever men who essay to judge books, should be so unfamiliar with the lives of the really poor as not to recognize the formidable quality of Trader Horn's position. Neither Dickens nor Dostoiefsky ever cut so cleanly or so deep to the very quick of the poverty problem as does Mr. Horn, who has dwelt "in the light of philanthropy." Here we have a character speaking without aid from art. In my review of *Trader Horn* I said it was like listening to a voice from the grave; as though a corpse were uttering astonishing apothegms. But every now and then one is uncomfortably aware that this old gentleman from the much-despised Victorian era is very much alive. We note that his remarks have a sting. It will take a whole generation of modern sophisticated American writers, for example, to live down that innocent-looking jibe of his about the *Mayflower* having "a refining influence upon history." Very few of the critics who wrote adversely of *Trader Horn* ever said anything as good as that. And we who write have to admit that Mr. Horn has the knack of stating our problems with the horrifying clarity of a precocious child. In this new volume he announces to Mrs. Lewis that for a while he had been "plot-locked" in his writing. If there is a better phrase to describe the predicaments a writer of fiction encounters in his daily toil I have yet to hear it.

But to me the most vivid interest centers about Mr. Horn's comments upon himself and his relations with civilization, "so called," as he puts it. He expresses for us more truly than has ever seemed possible the actual feelings of sensitive and casual poverty. He reveals the desperate and stupefying intolerance of the English poor, their pride, their fatalism and their shrewd psychological insight. In spite of Mr. Horn's constant allusions to *Homo stultus* he has a deep perception of the authentic agonies of the common folk who struggle to preserve in their poverty their self-respect and what we more fortunate beings call "personality." It is, he tells us, "not to every one's taste to give way to relief." Speaking of a soldier found dead of starvation near the new war memorial in Johannesburg, Mr. Horn says: "What all these committees are too ignorant to grasp is that those medals and testimonials he had in his pocket are just what killed him." He has a hard practical faith in what he calls "hereditary paramounts" as opposed to more democratic institutions, and in this he identifies himself with the submerged masses of Britishers who are fundamentally conservative and will always be the hidden reef on which communism and socialism suffer shipwreck. Mr. Horn knows a lot more about the proletariat than either Upton Sinclair or Bernard Shaw. But he remains for us a person of extraordinary interest because he is a genuine Rip Van Winkle of Victorian literature.

It is necessary to mention this unique feature of Mr. Horn's advent among us to-day not only because very few critics seem aware of it but because the object of this argument is to introduce the reader to a fantastic tale of boy-vikings and stirring deeds by land and sea in the dim dawn of history. Mr. Horn has many immovable convictions and not the least of these relates to his descent from the Norsemen who made a practice of raiding the British Isles. "The Old Fist-and-Spear" is a refrain that all readers of Mr. Horn's first book will remember. Mr. Horn's imagination is fundamentally heroic. The men and events of his own past assume almost legendary proportions in his mind. For his ancestors nothing short of Valhalla will do.

Harold the Webbed is the naïve fairy bed-time story of an aged adventurer who has preserved through a lifetime of extraordinary experiences, not all of them glorious, the fabulous imagination of a child. And it is the author's complete obliviousness of all modern literary technique which evokes in us an almost breathless fascination. Beneath the amusing assumption of knowledge which he has picked up from newspapers and motion pictures our author's mind is unaware of any literary movement later than the Rider Haggard of *Allan Quatermain* and *She*. In his conversation the people he has met become formidable, grandiose and mythological. And who will censure the old, tired hawker of kitchenware if, woven into the strange bright tapestry of his thoughts, we detect a strand or two of baser metal, such as his desire to please the Americans and a pathetic preoccupation with the cinema? Surely he is not the first Britisher to toy with either of these mundane problems.

"Come to that," he says, "what's a hearth without a roamer? Somebody to open the door that's not been expected?" That indeed is what Trader Horn has done. He has opened the door of the House of Letters and crept up to the hearth, not quite certain of his reception.

But he need have no fear.

WILLIAM MCFEE

Westport, Conn.

INTRODUCTION

READERS *of Aloysius Horn's first book will not need to be reminded that he is not only a stout Englishman but a staunch Lancastrian.* Harold the Webbed, *written in a poor-man's lodging-house in Johannesburg, is his hymn to an England he will never again see as he sees it beyond the crowding memories of a wanderer's life—stable as a boy's home is to him. Wherever he has roamed, whether in Mexico or in Madagascar, Abyssinia, America or round about Aden, one picture has gone with him, a vision of Lancaster in the Earlies;* his *earlies.*

Lancashire. A place where the aftermath of the Wars of the Roses is still a power to be felt: where the bowman forgets not his lore of the bow but waits for the Call to save England once again—when the Machine, like blind Samson, has destroyed itself in the general ruin brought about by its giant hands: a place where, above the roar of factories, the tide calls to its sleeping master the Viking and the gulls cry as they cried when that great figure first leapt ashore through the fierce protecting island surf. . . .

Lancashire in the Earlies. Aye!

So much for the story he has written. But in the conversations of this volume will be found a constant preoccupation not only with viking life but with

America, as if he could not forget that America and Lancashire are near neighbours compared, say, with America and Yorkshire, that barbarous country across the little River Hodder, where the White Rose still grows. Besides, as Aloysius Horn puts it, "A feller's wanderlust used to find plenty of scope in the States, whether in search of fact or fancy."

Lancashire, the States, London—so travels the vagrant shuttle of his memories.

The foregoing is the original preface as it was sent to the publishers with the manuscript of *Harold the Webbed.* I had a strong conviction that such a magnificent "Hornbook" as this is was a vintage strong enough to need no bush, and the less said by me the better. But now after receiving scores of letters from America demanding to know the "reactions" of Aloysius Horn to his new state of fame and material comfort and peace, and after a personal request from our publishers, I feel that the old man's great public would welcome a second instalment of the personal story begun in my necessarily long introduction to *Trader Horn.* I therefore must lay aside my personal conviction that a brief preface should be the only introduction of mine to this boyish and vivid story of youth in the earlies of old England, and I will try to capture a second impression of Trader Horn from the time that there came a tide in his affairs which, taken at the flood, led on to Fortune.

I have been told by American correspondents that they love the whole Horn episode because it is "such a Cinderella story." So indeed it is. My husband often says "People who doubt the romance of Aloysius Horn seem to forget that the improbable has never touched him more strongly than in his old age; when by entering a certain small gate in a certain South African town of thousands of gates on a certain morning of the week he became a famous man within a few months and known to a hundred thousand readers ten thousand miles across the sea from that little gate." Yes, it is impossible to shut one's eyes to the fact that a certain spirit of romance has walked close beside Aloysius Horn as it walks beside very few in these days of the Machine. For the old man's days were nearly over when he came shakily peddling to my door.

"As a tale that is told," says the Psalmist. By how small a margin was that actually told! The caretaker of the doss-house (who has a never-failing interest in the Cinderella story) told me only a few months ago that "that old gentleman had got to the last lap when he first went to your house." Rheumatism had been making it increasingly difficult for him to twist up his wires neatly and strongly into a saleable article: rheumatism plus habitual shortage of food. The old man was getting to the postcard stage of the ageing down-and-outer; a stage, I might say, which in the Golden City is often the preliminary to that period of desperate hunger when you "sell a bottle" to a native. (In this country if you sell alcohol to a native you go to prison for it when you are caught, as sooner or later you will be in a town where dozens of such cases are tried in a week in the Magistrate's Court.) What happens when postcards fail and you fight the temptation of selling a bottle is told by the old man himself in graphic language in the pages of this book. Yes, Trader Horn's steps were getting feebler and slower as he mounted the forbiddingly steep and bare staircase of the doss-house which, leading from the street door, says so chillingly at the top of it: "Do not ask for credit as refusal will only offend." More and more frequently came the days when he thought it policy to stay in bed rather than face cold or wet weather in the search for food. In plain words, he had been for the previous year or so, or even longer, day by day and week by week, underfed. Hence the waxen skin, the sunken cheek and feeble step. Hence too, I think, the premature childishness of which Trader Horn seemed cheerfully conscious, calling it his "gift of the gods." The last lap, as the caretaker calls it—that sad-faced expert in the last days of friendless old men in a gold-mining city.

In the Golden City it happens frequently that perfectly decent old gentlemen make an effort to be convicted three times for drunkenness in order to secure a comfortable corner in an inebriates' home. "I haven't tried that meself yet—got me family name to think of. 'Twould never do for a Fist-and-Spear to be got hold of in the newspapers—even if it does get you a reg'lar bed and a bit o' nice fishing. Aye, that inebriates'. . . . Better for old timers than the Nazareth Home. Fellers 've seen the world are not asking to end their days amongst a flock of good women and orphans. . . . Oh, aye, they're *good*—a hundred per cent gold in that old ore. But an old timer likes something a bit more familiar. He'll have enough o' heaven later on. Aye, those sisters walking about make you think too much of the latter end."

I have often been asked how a man like Trader Horn came to this state of utter destitution. I will reply to his readers by asking them if they remember the old fable of the ant and the cricket: the virtuous ant always laying up store for the winter (of which the Scotch trader Sinclair * is a fine example) and the careless cricket shrilling through life while he can and shouldering no responsibilities? There has been a good deal of the cricket in Aloysius Horn. He played at school—old schoolfellows of his who have read his book have written that his exercise books were scribbled all over with spears and assegais and savages, and that he "rushed up and down the corridors with his troop of braves"; he played on the West Coast—drilling natives he had dressed up in old Lancer jackets and dashing about with butterfly-nets and staring deep into the pellucid water of unsullied lakes; he has played all sorts of strange games in Madagascar and Mexico and along the Lake Chad Road and round about the shores of the Red Sea—for who shall say where, with him, has been the dividing line between his living and his fun?

An old Boer War acquaintance wrote recently of

* See *Trader Horn, Volume One.*

Aloysius Horn that, thirty years ago, he had "a long yellow moustache" and a "laugh like a mountain brook." Some other day I will give this same man's story of Trader Horn's breezy scorn of a certain English officer's efforts to sort out by the mere strength and variety of the oaths he was yelling at the native drivers an *impasse* of refractory army mules at a bad drift.* And how, having helped to disentangle the snarl of kicking, biting animals and their wagons, he "rode off rejoicing," and finally—turning his horse for a moment on a little eminence before disappearing into the dusty spaces of the veld—Aloysius put a stirrup-iron to his face as if he were screwing a monocle to his eye and bellowed: "You do it like this, bai Jove!" Or some such ribald remark.

Yes, Trader Horn has been a cricket, of rather violent tendencies perhaps, but certainly nearer to the cricket than the ant. Variety is the very salt of life to him still, even in the smallest matters; as when, last November, while staying under our roof, I got him to autograph a number of photos for his American friends before he left for England it was with great difficulty that I persuaded him to do the job in a uniform manner. He made a murmuring running comment somewhat on these lines: "I'm tired now of signing them below. I'll do this one just above my head." Or "This piece of my leg will do nicely to write it on." And again: "I'm going to put plain Aloysius to this . . . but this feller I'll give better value to." And he would

* Ford over a river.

write a flourishing "Alfred Aloysius Horn" with the glee and simplicity of a child pouring over a painting-book. If I did not watch him carefully his next variation might be a cold "A. A. Horn."

It is probable that, following this hunger for variety, Trader Horn has never, since he left the West Coast, spent more than three or four consecutive years in one spot. Like the rogue elephant, whose ways he knows so well, he is a wide ranger: hunting, prospecting for minerals from Abyssinia to the Cape; storekeeping in Rhodesia; bricklaying in Kentucky—a euphemism for making mash-tubs for moonshiners—painting pictures or inn signs indiscriminately as he tramps the States; catching African butterflies in his youth for collectors, and in his maturer years collecting mastodon bones for phosphates in Florida; and finally, tossing off the story of his youth and adventures and dashing into fiction about viking boys, when, again like the tragic rogue elephant, he is caught at last in the oozy marsh of poverty and age with no prospect of pulling himself out, Trader Horn is, as he would say, a "world-beater" in sheer variety.

I think the immediate cause of his getting caught fast in the Golden City was an accident he had seven years ago when in the rôle, for the moment, of bricklayer he fell from a low roof in Pretoria and damaged one leg very badly. It became septic and the doctors mentioned amputation. But the old man had faith in the charms of Egbo and used to do a little dabbling in the incantations and philtres of local Kaffir witch-doctors.

He still has the leg; troublesome, it is true, but a leg that can walk. One up to Egbo.

Such an accident at his age increased his feebleness very rapidly, and it can easily be seen that prospecting became a burden instead of a joy. As he has said in one of the books: "The boulders all seemed more than life-size." So he gradually turned his attention to prospecting round about Johannesburg with a load of wire goods—he who had been the king of the wild old prospecting days and knows Africa's mineral alphabet like a book!

"Oh, aye, the So-and-so Mountains. It's near there I found graphite." Or "There'll be oil fields there when the right man comes along."

Going for a hundred mile journey to Rustenburg just before I posted the first manuscript to London (he had felt the bitter Transvaal winter very badly, from June to August of 1926, and early in September I took him to a warm sleepy old Dutch town, whose traffic was nothing more violent than ox-wagons and an occasional Ford, for a month's rest under the eye of my brother who is commandant in that district) he entertained my daughter and me with a marvellous running comment on the landscape, which he read in terms of minerals. He had not been out of the Golden City for two or three years and was feeling like a wild animal freed from a trap. Every gap in the mountains, every outcrop on the nearer foothills, was familiar reading to him: "That means coal." "Boulders that shape mean. . . ." Or "You see that pass between those points? If you go through there and take the third turning to the left you'll come across some strange caves. Bat guano to sink a ship! Valuable stuff, but the natives'll not go near. There's other things besides bats and baboons in those old caves." (Perhaps nothing more mysterious than the bones of primitive and vanished tribes or eerie bushman drawings on the walls; but all habitats of the dead fill the native with dread.)

I once heard Trader Horn describe some place where there is mineral riches on the West Coast as "the second turning after you get past Samba Falls." Yes, he talks of this vast Africa, north, south, east and west, with the same matter-of-fact familiarity with which he talks of the Walworth division, London. The Elephant and Castle, London, is as clear in his mind as the elephants he has chased crossing borders into foreign territory. It was while he was a detective in Scotland Yard that he learnt certain parts of London so well. That four years in Scotland Yard were perhaps the longest period he has ever "stayed put" since leaving the Ivory Coast. The story of how and why he became a detective will come later. Briefly, it was because he had married "the bonny lass in ringlets" and felt that he ought then to make some effort to curb his roaming instincts. She was only sixteen. "Signed seventeen, of course, in the register," is how he puts it. More of this pretty story anon; except that "the bonny lass in ringlets" now lies quiet in an American city graveyard with a little daughter to keep her company.

To go back to the Scotland Yard period: the detective's life appealed to Aloysius Horn because there was always "something for a feller to chase." The capture did not always appeal to him so much as the chase. It was the wives of the prisoners he could not face: "They look at you so. . . . Aye, ma'am—when a woman cries and you're taking away her man . . . don't tell me that's a life for a gentleman."

And that was why Trader Horn left Scotland Yard of his own accord with a good record. Perhaps I could add something to that good record one day which will make it not quite so good as a record of a conscientious detective but an extremely lovable human document of a boyish young man of tender heart and generous impulse.

He subsequently was obliged to earn his living for a time as a detective in the States, and frequent mentions of his experiences there will be found in this book and in a third Hornbook to follow.*

I have been unable to trace the year in which Aloysius Horn first took his wife to America. There must have been some years in which she was left in England with a child, or two children: I refer to the period when, following the call that attracts all roamers, Horn came out to the great goldfields then recently discovered in the Transvaal, South Africa: those enormously rich fields which after forty years

*Readers will remember that the hornbook was the quaint primer or reader (an oaken board on which the alphabet, numerals and the Lord's Prayer were set out and covered with thin horn to preserve them) from which our ancestors learned to spell. In my family we have accidently adopted the word as a convenient collective name for Trader Horn's books.

still produce gold to the value of four million pounds a month and have incidentally produced the Golden City as the capital town on a long reef of smaller townships. He was again, or still, in South Africa when the Boer War broke out ten years later. During that period he had prospected for diamonds, platinum, oil, graphite, asbestos, copper, coal and tin; had been trader and storekeeper in Rhodesia; had been big-game hunting in Rhodesia and Matabeleland from time to time. In connection with this, his readers might like to hear that the old man has a tremendous scar round his ribs which he casually and obligingly disclosed to an admiring audience in our drawing-room one evening just before he left for England. It is the mark of a bad mauling by a lion from whose attack he was saved by "old Tom Connolly" putting a bullet into the lion. Tom Connolly at the same moment put one into his friend's shoulder, it being difficult at the time to sort out the combatants. That bullet, so a doctor told us who has attended Trader Horn from time to time when we called him in, is still in the old man's shoulder. That he did not die from blood-poisoning—the great danger after such maulings—the Trader, with simple faith, puts down to Egbo. The wound, after thirty years, more or less, still aches in cold weather.

Old Tom Connolly twice saved his comrade "from the jaws of the lion." "Aye," says the old man, with an engaging candour that ignores the prohibitionist, "I was lying in me cups one night under a wagon and Tom was asleep there by the fire. Something woke him, and he sat up just in time to see a lioness lying on her back trying to tickle me with her paws. Gentle as a kitten she was. I might a been a bobbin o' cotton. Oh, aye—old Tom. . . . One of the best." With Egbo and Tom Connolly in partnership the world has something to be thankful for.

Trading, hunting, prospecting, storekeeping: yet when the Boer War broke out Aloysius Horn was doing none of these things. He was, in his capacity as bricklayer and cement expert, making not a mash-tub for illicit whiskey but a niche in a wall for a lady who wanted a statue of the Virgin in her room. I picture my old friend quietly manipulating the trowel, pipe in mouth and peace in his eye, and feeling rather happy and good over a task that apppealed to his Catholic soul. I picture him going with his peaceful reawakened Catholic thoughts into the bars and the quiet colonial streets at the end of the day's work and finding the light of war in men's eyes. Within a week he had joined Prince Albert's Guards, the local regiment of that part of Cape Colony. But eventually he found his right niche as one of "Kitchener's cattle thieves," that small handful of daredevil men and natives whose duty it was to commandeer all cattle from the Boer farms and herd them along as prisoners of war. The herd grew to many thousands and was shepherded hundreds of miles on the way to headquarters.

"Aye, the Boer snipers could never spot us, when we dismounted in the middle of a herd like that. The biggest danger was getting a bullet in your back from a farm window as you were leaving. Poor things. . . . But we never took Pansy away. . . . Beg pardon, ma'am? Oh, Pansy . . . Well, I mean the family cow that seemed to be the right one for the children's milk. We always left one for the children and we always called her Pansy."

Trader Horn in the rôle of gentleman-soldier!

It must have been some time after the Boer War that Trader Horn first went to Madagascar. After sundry interesting adventures there he seems to have drifted to England again and to have gone to the States for the second time. But whether his wife went with him the first or the second time I have not been able to discover. She died after a certain Fourth of July; that I know because he "carried her out on the porch to see the fireworks." Poor little ringletted one—rushed through life like a little white cockleshell of a boat tied to the *Flying Dutchman,* or some such wandering galleon pirate or ship!

After her death he had a period in Morocco—some job connected with railway construction there, a very distant connection I suspect it to have been—and from there I think he must have drifted over towards Abyssinia and Aden and eventually down the coast to Zanzibar. But when the Great War broke out he was in the Southern States again with his daughter, not long married, and son-in-law. His only son too was somewhere in the offing, the boy who was destined to die in Mesopotamia. It was after the death of this boy and, as I think, a coolness with his daughter, consequent upon his losing her little boy Sandy in the streets of London, that Trader Horn again turned his face towards Africa and came out once more to his old prospecting, roaming life. Platinum was probably booming—there is always something calling to prospectors from this rich bosom of old Africa. The Transvaal, Rhodesia, Madagascar again, back to the Transvaal and the fall from a roof which for ever stopped his ranging days as they once had been. The old elephant was caught in the swamp at last. This, roughly speaking, is the itinerary of Trader Horn as near as I can get it.

I should like at this point to give some idea of the extreme haziness about dates in the mind of Trader Horn. I picture his brain as resembling that of an old lion when he suns himself on a rock in the last days of life, seeing his past as a series of blurred scenes alternating between hunt and kill, sleep and play and roaming. That this haziness is a genuine one is proved, I think, by the following incident: He said one day during conversation "when we were waiting in London for the Great War, nineteen hundred and two." I said: "But you mean the Boer War, don't you? That was the year of the peace, though, so it doesn't fit." To which he replied testily: "No, I don't mean the Boer War. Nothing of the sort. I know it was the Great War because my son-in-law and my son had come over to London to join up, and my daughter was there with Sandy. We'd all come over from the States after the war broke out. Nineteen hundred and two that was." When I proved to him that he was wrong in his date, he said peevishly: "Oh, well, have it your own way then."

Sandy. . . . I cannot pass the name Sandy without quoting here from the story of Aloysius Horn's departure from South Africa which I recently wrote for a woman journalist:

> "I have to-day heard the reason for Aloysius Horn's hasty departure for England last week. It seems that his only daughter, who has heard nothing of her father for ten years, recognised his portrait in an illustrated paper, got the book, and wrote to him there and then—a hearty letter, which Mrs. Lewis describes as 'friendly as a boy's.'
>
> "It begins philosophically: 'I thought you were about due, dad. Nearly two years ago I began to think you must be on the way, but I expected to see you on my own doorstep, not some one else's. . . . If it's books you're wanting to make, dad, don't forget Georgia. Do you remember when you and I painted the portrait of Ben Edward's racehorse, and he paid us for it with two backs of pork?'
>
> "Mrs. Lewis tells me that this refers to a period in the old man's career about which she has many notes.
>
> "The daughter enclosed a photo of herself and five charming children: Sandy, Veronica, Trinita, Eleanor and the baby who, luckily, is called Aloysius after his wandering grandfather, and who—says his mother—is naughty but lovable. Like the earlier Aloysius, one imagines. And next to the big boy,

Sandy, aged sixteen, two Spanish school friends of his, which, to those who have read the book, sounds very much like history repeating itself.

"Mrs. Lewis tells me she has often heard of Sandy, the only grandchild born when last Aloysius Horn saw his daughter. Not once but a score of times during the last two years has he lamented that if only he hadn't lost Sandy he would have not had this long rift with his daughter. It seems that during the Great War, when all the family had gathered to 'join up' in various forms, the old man inadvertently mislaid the child in the streets of London! Sandy was lost, definitely lost, for many hours—hours which the guilty grandfather has never forgotten—until a big policeman brought him home at midnight, sleepy but smiling at the importance of being out with a policeman in broad darkness. It seems that grandfather had been watching the aeroplanes going over to France, and when at last he came to earth again 'the child is not, and I—whither shall I go?' as the Bible inimitably puts the story of another lost one.

"However, all is wiped out now, and the old man is on the way to a wonderful Christmas in the bosom of his grandchildren—not forgetting the presents for their stockings.* Seen safely aboard by a discreet

* Those Christmas stockings: I had come back from a day's shopping for the journey laden, as I thought, with everything necessary for the stockings and no one forgotten. But after spreading out the treasures—the Zulu bangles for the little granddaughters, the beautifully sculptured snake in black clay made in a native kraal in Basutoland, the oxhide shield and assegai from Natal for Sandy, the carved animal from Rhodesia for baby Aloysius—the old man looked at me accusingly and said: "And those two Spanish lads? Where's theirs? Poor lads, they're far from their home, they mustn't be left

friend, and, with the proceeds of his book, travelling first class, with a new trunk full of new clothes, Aloysius Horn once more makes a quiet 'getaway' from Africa. He has always said he never goes home without some money in his pocket, and once more he follows this little rule of his. Not 'ivories' this time but that imponderable something called a living that has been distilled from his pathetic attempt at a book.

"But it was no easy matter to keep the old man in Africa for nearly three weeks while he sat for his portrait by Mr. Percival Small, who was at work on the painting within twenty-four hours after landing at Durban, and was still putting in the last touches within five hours of his sitter's departure from Johannesburg. The old man's frank impression of the artist is that he is a 'top notcher,' and that his picture of Trader Horn is his 'banner picture.' Further, he works like hell; might 'a been weaving out a poem by the looks of him, and puts 'enough energy into it to build a mash-tub for moonshiners when the revenuers are expected.' And not for any other feller living would he have waited three weeks when there was a nest of new babies to go and see over there!"

I must now think more definitely how to reply to all those American readers of Trader Horn's who in their letters have asked me to tell them what the re-

out." He was remembering Peru and the nabobs from Hayti. I accordingly added two wooden daggers, finely carved with a negro's head as handle (East Africa), and then all was complete for the visit of Father Aloysius Christmas.

actions of the old man are to his extraordinary change of fortune. I think the simplest way to do this is to quote from some of his letters written to me from Durban in July and August of 1927. After Mr. Galsworthy's visit to Johannesburg, when he interviewed the Trader (February, 1927), it had become increasingly clear that not only for the sake of his health, which always suffered in the severe Transvaal winter, but to give his editor a rest, I had by that time, sixteen months after first meeting Aloysius Horn, collected material for three volumes and was becoming mentally exhausted by the constant proximity of that human treasure chest—we must get the old man away from Johannesburg for a time! So, on April 2nd, after rescuing him from a rapacious landlord and keeping him quietly at our house for the day—as quietly as we could keep a seafaring man who had been separated too long from his element—we saw him off in the evening to Durban and the Indian Ocean.

As a little group of us stood saying goodbye to that happy old face framed in the train window a remarkable-looking elderly man came up, peered closely at Aloysius Horn through thick glasses, and exclaimed "Why, it's Zambesi Jack!" The two shook hands as only old timers can and, turning to us, the newcomer said: "This is Zambesi Jack, whose life beats Rider Haggard's fiction hollow. Somebody ought to write a book about him." I felt pleased that *Trader Horn* was already not only written but accepted in London, although not yet in New York. But I said nothing; it seemed too big a subject to begin at the moment.

This gentleman was Major X——, also an old timer, and, I am told by Trader Horn, a man of aristocratic birth. There was something about him which made you forget his shabby clothes, of which an old khaki shirt was the dominant note. Eager brown eyes, bright and boyish, set in a deeply tanned face, looked out at the world over a strange curly and grizzled beard which hung in straight lines from the cheekbones but not very far below the chin; like a picture of Jove he was.

I felt extremely pleased at the unexpected testimony of this strange being to the extraordinary nature of Aloysius Horn, for he was obviously not only "gentleman born," as the old expression has it, but knew Africa as Zambesi Jack knows it. (Major X——, by the way, is not one of the nine elderly gentlemen who, in addition to a lady from Texas, have written or called on me with a view to having their adventures edited—adventures, they say, which knock Trader Horn's into a cocked hat—to whom I have been painfully obliged to reply that it is not adventures which make the Hornbooks—a man might go to Mars and make a very dull literary job of it—but it is their philosophy, their wisdom and that spontaneous love of nature and human nature which endears the writer to his enormous public.)

Now, when Trader Horn had been sunning himself in Durban for two months, things began to happen in New York. The Literary Guild cabled that it had chosen *Trader Horn* as its book of the month for June; and after a lightning manufacture of the book such as could never happen in staid old London, the post, six weeks later, brought six copies of the beautiful Guild edition. Within half an hour of its arrival I wrapped up one copy for my old friend and rushed out to post it without delay. For I had always had ringing in my ear a forlorn saying of his some months earlier: "At my age slips come easy. I'd like just to handle the book before I die." I addressed that first edition of *Trader Horn* to the Durban Men's Home, which was a cheap place for sailors and old timers, where Aloysius was living very happily on ten dollars a month.

The arrival of a fat cheque from the Guild was an immense relief to me, for I had for many months been getting deeper and deeper in debt trying to keep the old man afloat and, of course, not earning very much with journalism while I was so completely absorbed in the notes I was taking from him. (None the less, in that difficult eighteen months of struggle, in addition to finishing an interrupted novel, I wrote several short stories and about twenty articles to keep the South African jackal from the door and completed, within eleven months after meeting the old man, his first book, *Trader Horn*.)

At one time, shortly before Mr. Galsworthy turned up to turn our pumpkins into coaches with a wave of his pen, I had even been driven to offer the manuscript of *Trader Horn* as a serial to a local newspaper. Fortunately—oh, very fortunately for the old man and his editor—the local newspaper smiled in that superior way local newspapers have and said no, they knew those old down-and-outers; scores of 'em. There was no reason to suppose I had discovered anything better than they could have found out for themselves. In fact, nothing doing. I then put all my pride in my pocket and begged for a job on the newspaper that could bring me in five pounds a month which would be enough to keep the old man afloat. "Even only for six months," I said. (I had for some years been doing free-lance journalism—"so called," as Aloysius would say—on that same newspaper.) But the cruel editor said, disregarding my passionate plea, and looking at his watch by that time, that he really couldn't promise anything but he'd let me know. I am still waiting for that message. Shortly after the publication of the book in England this same newspaper which had refused the manuscript published an article on "Literary Impostors": Louis de Rougemont, and so on. And, while just keeping clear of the law of libel, the writer, in the second paragraph, gently, elusively, carelessly, ruminatingly, mentioned Aloysius Horn and his editor. I have noticed before that the resentment people and newspapers feel from the treatment of others is nothing like so severe as the resentment they feel after their own mistakes. I should like, later on,* to return to this subject

* Yes, at some later date: for this is a subject on which I write very fluently and with immense enjoyment.

of the literary impostor, for I have had "passages" with two great English papers on the delicate subject of authenticity. At present I must keep to the subject of Aloysius Horn, the man with money in his pocket and fame on his brow.

It might all have been so near to tragic failure had Galsworthy not come to Johannesburg to see Trader Horn. For not only did he silence the mouths of those who were delightedly willing to shriek "Impostor!"; he was such a true friend in the patient way he took pencil and paper and went through the business aspects of our future: in the way he asked innumerable questions about publishers and agents, agreements and contracts, suggesting this and altering that and himself writing and cabling to London on the matter (for, as Aloysius wrote to me from Durban: "I think Mr. Galsworthy's advice [the Foreword] worth a King's Ransom as he is not only the literrary Genius of our time but a Lawyer as well,"), and finally left me a precious cheque to keep the old man afloat from month to month "until the money comes in." It says much for Mr. Galsworthy's literary judgment that he prophesied "pots of money from a book like that." And true enough the first pot arrived within four months of the day on which he used those words, and it came from America.*

* If from time to time in this introduction I have told or quoted things pertaining to my own share in the shaping of Trader Horn's career which good manners, business etiquette or modesty should have left unsaid I can only say that—living as the Hornbooks have compelled me to live, at the mercy of grim but not always accurate journalists and hectic publicity people, and open to the ingenuous and often searching questions of scores of unknown correspondents, and, in addition to all this, living at so great a distance from America—I have had to be very much more communicative, and

Now I am going to be very frank with our American friends and tell them what a difficult time I had handling Trader Horn's share of the money while he was still wandering beatifically about Africa before his daughter and Sandy turned up to clarify matters. (And this for the American correspondents who enquire, very humanly and properly, whether "the old man is getting any royalities." To put it very bluntly once and for all—we are halving all profits.

Another matter before I finish the parenthesis: those fabulous sums alluded to so freely in the American newspapers do not pour in upon us week by week, as the innocent may well suppose from some of the paragraphs I have read. They *will* pour, all in good time; but I do think the public should be instructed—it would at least make it much easier for me were they so instructed—that it is a publisher's right and proper privilege not to hand over the profits of a book to its authors for nine months (that is in order to enhance those profits by wide and expensive advertising), and those nine months are not yet complete since the appearance of *Trader Horn* *).

So the complete "reactions" of Trader Horn to the full tide of his fortune will not be apparent until the book returns are made up in a month or so. None the less, with the unwonted and generous advances of our publishers and the sum made from the Literary Guild I

very much franker, than a year ago I should have deemed myself capable of being. Moreover, it is hard not to respond with open heart to so much joyous and friendly appreciation as has been shown by American readers.

* Written Feb. 8, 1928.

still had a certain amount of difficult manipulation, which I strove also to make discreet, before the joyful news arrived that he had a daughter waiting for him in England. And until Aloysius Horn got to England to spend Christmas with her and his new grandchildren he never even knew the extent of his fortune. He trusted me like a child, but I felt that it was incumbent upon me to keep from him the extent of his "prospector's luck," as he called it, while he was still within reach of old companions of the doss-house days and other too-merry souls. They gave him no peace when they thought he had struck a rich vein. Sometimes these street friends of his used to hint to Zambesi Jack that he was perhaps being badly used by "that lady." But he was scornfully loyal—I am glad to remember this—in those days when all was still uncertain to him. Uncertain, but, oh, how vastly exciting! On one occasion a leading communist, the sort of fellow who wears a pallid face and lank black hair, approached him in a bar and said to him in the usual manner: "Look here, old man—that Mrs. So-and-so living up there in her grand house [My poor little bungalow!], how's she treating you? What do *you* get out of it? Because if you're not getting your Just Rights you've only got to come to us about it. *We'll* back you," etc.

Trader Horn, who, like most men of good old family, remains a Tory to the bone, and has often entertained me with violent expressions of distaste and graphic descriptions of the Sunday night communist meetings in the streets of Johannesburg, replied to this noble offer (so he told my husband): "That lady doesn't owe me a penny. She bought what I wrote for her and paid me regularly. But now she's giving me enough to live on in comfort till the end of my days." He added some biting comments on "business fellers" which I will omit. This was his attitude at a time when he was only getting twelve to fifteen pounds a month from the sales of the book: the time when I was still hoping to hear the whereabouts of his daughter who he had told me was in the States and whose address I had for many months been trying to trace through friends in America * To an old man who had been quite penniless sixty or seventy dollars a month was riches, and to let him down gently into the waters of affluence was, in my opinion and that of common-sense men who advised me, an absolute necessity if one wished to avoid undue excitement and the temptation to spend and lend riotously in old haunts in Johannesburg and elsewhere.

In one of his amusing letters written to me from Durban Aloysius Horn alludes very prettily to his income as his "life pension for literary work."

It is my hope at some later date to publish the old man's letters written from Durban and elsewhere, of which I have many, including some charming ones addressed to my son and daughter. In the mean time I cannot refrain from quoting from the letter (July 7, 1927) written on receiving his Literary Guild copy, which was the first to arrive out here:

* His daughter eventually discovered her father through seeing his portrait in the *Illustrated London News*.

"You have just hit the nail on the head, as this of course will be read by royalty and the Coroneted. . . . I look forward to your name being Emblazoned in Literrary History in the not far distant future either. . . . You have a marvelous gift of Style which takes a hold of a reader which no one I ever read had and this is a Priceless Gift of him who presides and rules over all. . . . I thank you from the souls deabth for mentioning George Bussy * chum of Charles Dickens who have both crossed the Devide. . . . I was astonished what could be done by adding Conversational matter it is the best book I ever read thanks to your addition of the notes which are the real making of A. A. Horn. . . . You can rest assured that all honour acrouing from the book is justly yours."

And this after reading one or two of the first American reviews:

"I received the cuttings and think the contents really Sublime. Who would have thought it it's a Corker. . . . I think it the luckiest claim I ever pegged. . . . Youve sure got your Discovery notice up right in the center of the bigest literrary Diamond mine you could dream of Prospectors luck I call it."

* Readers of *Trader Horn* will be interested to hear that in December last I received a letter from a grandson of the George Bussy who was so dear to Aloysius Horn. He corroborates the place of his grandfather's abode in London (Albany Road) as given by the old man, also that he was Master of Hansard. His full name, which is also that of his grandson, now living in London, was George Thomas Moir Bussy.

His readers will like to know how Trader Horn varied his way of living as his income grew from nothing a year to sixty or seventy dollars a month. In the first place, he certainly never bought clothes with it; these were supplied for two years by my men folk. And in the second place, he never went to anything better in the way of a boarding-house than Salvation Army men's homes or the men's home in Durban already mentioned, any of which establishments cost him about two pounds (ten dollars) a month. And yet the balance of his income at that time would disappear in three weeks or so. There was no end to the treating and being treated. And the greatest treat of all for Trader Horn was to "get his hand down" for some poor down-and-outer such as he so recently had been himself. And no better way to spend a fortune if you are alone in the world.* But now that the old Trader has been handed over in good order to his daughter these restrictions no longer exist. I see indications, some of them very strange ones, of a complete surprise when he was told by my agent in London—who met the old gentleman at Tilbury—just what he had earned for himself by selling a gridiron.

To return to these reactions: not only would the Trader never buy a garment or in any way alter his appearance when he became a "pensioner for literrary work" but he took the very worst possible care of the clothes with which my men folk kept him supplied

*I have a delightful letter from the Superintendent of the Durban home in which he speaks of Mr. Horn as "a dear old gentleman who badly needs some one to take care of him."

before money came in and of any garments I had to buy him new. For instance, he was packed off to Durban with quite a nice little outfit of clothes, the best we could afford before we knew our luck in America. Extras were added to it from time to time during the six months. But when he arrived back in September, a famous man, he had only a few deplorable remnants left in a kitbag, all mixed up with his prayer book, his paintbox, the first edition of *Trader Horn* and some of the first American reviews which he found so vastly entertaining. His clothes had never been cleaned, nothing was sent to the wash (although when in the doss-house he had observed doss-house etiquette and washed his shirt on Sunday mornings) and he had lost, given away or sold quite a number of things including his winter overcoat and a travelling blanket. Two days after his arrival in Johannesburg as a successful man, I happened to jump out of a tram and walk down the road towards my gate. A familiar figure was walking down in front of me. It was Trader Horn. He had by that time got rid even of his socks and was marching along in fine happy mood chewing tobacco and looking thoroughly disreputable. However, if a rich man can not afford to look disreputable then nobody can. It is one of the privileges of success, and a very fine one too.

Still, it is hardly a privilege of which I wished him to take advantage when, a prodigal father, he was about to return to his daughter after ten years' absence. It was in order to circumvent this possibility that I bought Trader Horn's going-away wardrobe myself.

Let me tell a story arising out of this fact which will add grace to this narrative and perhaps place it on a higher literary plane than it might otherwise achieve.

I have discovered that old gentlemen are very difficult things to dress. Not perhaps when of the English military type or the strong, silent, aging, hundred-percenter of New York. There is a formula for such types easy to follow. But an old gentleman with a beard! . . . A literary old gentleman! . . . well, of course! He must have an old-fashioned inverness cape such as all the literary Victorians wore so effectively. A cape made, if possible, of rough grey Irish tweed with a doggish suggestion of a big check woven in it.

A Victorian old gentleman with a beard! . . . Well, of course—a soft black hat of poetic build, such as Tennyson. . . . Yes, and a wide shepherd's shawl or plaidie for the shoulders to enclose the beard in winter weather.

I saw it all—and then I looked at the Golden City and felt that the vision splendid could never be brought to reality in such an environment. Yet, with a month for the search, I began hunting round and poking about and putting leading questions to stupefied tailors. "An inverness? But madam, I can assure you they are *not* worn. Let me show you a nice range we have for elderly. . . ." Or it would be: "A *black* hat, madam? What age did you say? Oh, a clergyman, you mean. . . . Not a clergyman? Oh, then in that case we have just what you want in grey felt! . . ."

After a week's search I began to despair. I then entered a store which eventually did try to solidify my ideas with some degree of intelligence. I found a tailor who did not gape at the word inverness. Yes, he had seen pictures of them. Just the thing for an old gentleman—gave 'em dignity like. It is true I had to be content without that hint of a big check, and the cloth was far too smooth and close, with none of the romantic homespun quality about it. Still, it served. The tailor came up to the house and measured Trader Horn for the cape and for a thick cheviot suit calculated to defy the bitter east winds of Tilbury Docks in January. I found the wide, soft plaidie. I found a black hat: not the Tennysonian hat of my dreams, but still—it was a soft black hat. I looked at it thoughtfully as the young man held it out. What did it remind me of? Not Tennyson; it missed the poetic rake of the brim. Not an English parson—that jolly, adaptive headgear. Not . . . it looked more smug than any of these. Closer, less frank of outline. . . .

"If I were you, madam," said the thoughtful voice of the young man, "I would perhaps not mention to Mr. Horn for whom we stock this shape. To tell you the truth, we sell them to the Dutch *predikants.*"* Our eyes met guiltily. "Thank you," I said fervently. "Thank you."

Yes, the only sin I feel conscious of at present in my entire dealings with Aloysius Horn is that I let Trader Horn, buccaneer and big game hunter and the author

* Predikant—a minister of the Dutch Church.

of a successful book, go home to England in a Dutch *predikant's* hat.

It was this same young salesman, a tall good-looking boy of twenty or so, who vastly enjoyed the fun of clothing Aloysius Horn, who, when I first tried to explain my sartorial vision to him, said ruminatingly: "An inverness, madam . . . a black hat—a soft one. . . . Why, madam, you mean like Thomas Carlyle, do you not?"

My quest was over; here was one of the cognoscenti smiling understanding at me. Who says we are Philistines in the Golden City!

Talking about reactions: one of the quaintest and most touching effects of his own literary doings was that Trader Horn tried to get notes and experiences from other old men for my benefit. Or he would collect sea chanties for me at the docks in Durban. It was his way of doing his bit and I naturally encouraged the process and supplied him with pencils (of the blackest and softest), foolscap, envelopes and stamps. His efforts were not often successful, and I have known him to get furious with men from whom he had thought to get stuff of literary value. Quite a strange and, to me, very pathetic episode arising from this helpful habit of Trader Horn's happened at Durban. It was indeed a literary quarrel in the grand style between two gentlemen of the old school, one of whom lived under a boat and ran errands for sailors by way of living and the other was an old gentleman called Aloysius Horn who had taken refuge in a home for indigent men. Some day

I hope to give this precious fragment of life to the world, but not here. Suffice it to say (as Trader Horn would write) that the word gentleman used of the old derelict under the boat is meant in all seriousness.

Other interesting items of the Durban period I recorded in a letter to the publishers written in September, 1927, from which I quote here: "He apparently fled from Durban because he was being followed by wasters, knowing they could get a drink from him or 'touch' him for half a crown or a shirt or a pair of trousers—anything in that kitbag except the prayer book or the paintbox or his copy of *Trader Horn.*"

After living so long in the shadow of philanthropy it is indeed a joy for Zambesi Jack to be able to give like a gentleman. No "meat tickets" for him. He believes in unorganised charity, whether as giver or receiver. "Unorganised" is a mild word. I think "riotous" would be better for that reckless disposal of wardrobe and other trifles which characterises Trader Horn as a cheerful giver. All this might be possible in a better world, but unfortunately in this world literally to give all that thou hast leads to complications.

A friend who had been keeping an eye on the old man while in Durban tells us that when a cheque arrived he cashed it in a small and friendly store, left the money with the storekeeper and returned every day for a pound until it was gone. Of the money that was sent him to buy necessary summer clothes or to move to a decent boarding-house not one cent has been spent on either of these aids to the genteel life of an author.

I have recently visited the caretaker of the Johannesburg doss-house in which Trader Horn wrote his first and second books. He told me the same story of generosity and the inability to save the old man from himself. He also told me that when the house was very full and noisy, especially on Sundays, the old man would come to his office (a small and dingy apartment at the top of the stairs) and beg for a quiet hour or two in which to do a little writing. A space would then be cleared on the table which was full of sordid oddments, such as handleless cups and so on, and the caretaker tried to keep the door shut against the other lodgers.

His life in Durban has apparently varied from the quiet and homely routine of the old man in the home to a hectic existence on the sea front or marine parade, where ladies in motors waved to him or took him for drives in which they discussed life and the hereafter: where he met strange men who invited him to sup with them: and where the chorus arose, "Good morning, Mr. Horn!" "Let me pay for that one, Mr. Horn!" "My turn now, I think, Mr. Horn!"

And when finally an unknown lady rushed out from one of the hotels and kissed the old man in the street, he went to the station and booked his return passage to Johannesburg (September 5, 1927).

The appearance of all our conversations in his book was a great surprise to Trader Horn, for he had believed with the most delightful naïveté and ignorance even to the length required to make a book, that his written account of his doings on the West Coast was quite voluminous enough to form what publishers would call a full-length book. He thought the same later of his viking story; and who shall wonder at it when you consider where it was written, either sitting on his bed in the doss-house or perhaps on congested Sundays mornings in the caretaker's little office (which was also his bedroom) on a table littered with a collection of sordid objects?

One thing I am anxious should be plainly understood, and that is that all the material for both Volume Two and Volume Three was collected before *Trader Horn* was published.* They are therefore as fresh and innocently unspoilt by the excitement of success as in *Trader Horn.* This, I have always felt, gives a peculiar value to the three books, that, to one not less than the others belongs that bloom of innocence and unself-consciousness which, once success arrived, could never be recovered. After he had completed his West Coast narrative the old man went pathetically and eagerly on with the other manuscripts in case he should lose a very pleasant living. A modest bird in the hand was to a penniless man so much more real than the most brilliant bird in the bush.

The Trader knew of course that I was taking notes of all his talk, but had a vague idea that it was for "the newspapers." The part I was to play in the actual book

* That is to say, the old man had written his slender stories as bases, and I had taken full notes from his talk about them. So, as I wrote in September last to my publishers, when certain sceptical reviewers in England (and perhaps a few in America) are "asked to believe" that Aloysius Horn is going to write another book they can, if necessary, be reassured as to how it is done.

was to correct his spelling and supply commas and, if necessary, the love light and the ladies' dresses and a sunset or two. I never argued the point but let him believe that I was adding the love lights and the sunsets. Whereas, of course, what I did was to preserve his manuscript as it was and go on talking and taking notes. In those days Aloysius Horn was very near to childishness from the pressure of too many lean years, and it was both confusing to him and tedious to me to discuss details with him. For this reason he never saw a page of his again after once he had given it to me, nor did I even show him the typescript of it when the book was ready for the publishers. I was always afraid that a little overexcitement might stop the even flow of his awakened mind. So, although he met Mr. Galsworthy on the stoep and discussed the influence of the Malay civilization east and west from the Malay Archipelago, he never knew that a foreword was being written to the book. Such words as "publisher," "foreword," "agent," and so on, were Greek to him. To Aloysius Horn, in the making of a book, only two persons were necessary—a writer and a printer.

I shall never cease to be thankful that I was able to collect enough for three books from a source so completely untouched by the world of business, by material success and the heady adulation of strangers. I have often been asked how I managed to get down the old man's talk in such detail. (As far as his style goes, I have just received a letter from a London journalist, writing in excited vein after a first visit to Aloysius

Horn just arrived in the bosom of his family, assuring me that "the way I have caught the flavour of his speech is nothing less than genius." I suppose Boswell had also to content himself with this reflective or mirrorlike brand of genius.) And as this is a question which I am sure is in the mind of my readers, and on which I have had to defend myself against a few suspicious reviewers who unconsciously pay my attainments a compliment they little deserve, I should like to explain my methods here.

In the first place, I kept two notebooks. Carrying Notebook No. 1 to the stoep with me, and armed with a pencil, I would find the old man just arrived, sitting happily in his chair enjoying the peace and the sunshine. First he would hand me a roll of foolscap and exhibit every sign of impatience until I had taken it inside and read it. I would then supply him with some tobacco while I took away the manuscript to read in my room. After reading it quickly I would return and discuss with him what he had written, sitting at a small garden table with Notebook No. 1 opened before me. During the discussion of what he had written the talk would digress in unexpected ways, very much as a lively young heifer will bolt into various gateways when she is being driven through the village. At first I missed a deplorable lot of good stuff through not having completed my method. But week after week I grew better at it as the technique of my own home-made shorthand improved. The old man would use a racy expression or utter some profound and fresh observation. This

I would get down in my rude hieroglyphs and abbreviations. After ten minutes' talk or so I would pretend that I heard the telephone or that there was a cake burning in the oven and leave him to smoke a bit. I would then go to my room where Notebook No. 2 was laid out on my desk and into that fairer page add the details to each sentence I found in Notebook No. 1 and which would have been forgotten if I trusted to my memory. After completing the batch I would return to the stoep and take up the thread of the talk again with Notebook No. 1. Another fifteen minutes or so and I would again disappear to my room. This would go on for perhaps three or four hours at a time, and often twice a week. For although officially he was only supposed to come on Monday mornings he would often appear about Thursday as well if he had had a "new idea" likely to intrigue Americans or when he felt lonely and sick of the doss-house. He generally arrived about half past ten and departed about half past two, after having had lunch and a very lingering progress towards the gate.

On his final departure with his weekly earnings in his pocket I would return to my desk and go carefully over all the notes of that day in Notebook No. 2, adding such pearls as generally fell when he was loitering over the gate before his return to the drab realities of the Golden City. And all that day and during the next morning, especially on waking up early, I was able to hear again things that had escaped me and to piece together the whole tapestry. The turmoil in my head on Monday nights is indescribable: I could often have screamed at the sight of other old timers creeping up my steps as they do daily in this city. The safest thing for me to do on a Monday night was to go to a theatre or the pictures or play bridge. And in the afternoon, as soon as my notes were finished, to go and play a vigorous game of tennis. Indeed, I have never done so much thèatregoing and sought other amusements as while I have been occupied with the Hornbooks.*

I think I should add that sometimes the old man looked very suspiciously at my notebooks and pencil. "Now, don't send that to those newspapers," he would say. Or "You'll crucify me with those notes." Meaning: "You'll make enemies for me."

Talking of making enemies by frank criticism: it has been said by many English critics that Aloysius Horn has "some brilliant jibes at Americans." This is a mistaken idea of the character of the man. If he speaks of Americans as being a moral people except when it comes to murder and so on it is said in perfect simplicity. Sarcasm is a weapon for which Aloysius Horn has a supreme contempt. His attitude, expressed in his own vernacular, is roughly this: "A moral people, Americans. Of course if now and then somebody gets killed, well—we're all nothing but human. Such things will happen where men are still men." Trader Horn,

* In September last I wrote to my publishers "Even now, after six months' rest from interviews with the old man while he is away at the sea, I feel very strongly that I could never again go through such a strain, even if it were possible to get him to talk when he and I were both unknown, and he was just a friendless old man, pouring out his repressions and impressions—and expressions. (The only thing I never heard him pour out was depressions.)"

after such things as he has seen in his youth on the Ivory Coast, and later in his ranging stride up and down Africa, is not likely to feel faint over a murder or two.

And all this care of his to please the American market (I have had this put down to me, who have never been to the States), what is it but the most engagingly transparent guile? Were I asked to analyse the charm of his speech I should say that it lies less in a guileless simplicity than in the simplicity of his guile. But it is not guile when he speaks of the American as moral. He means it, murders and all. He has not a jibe in him. Trader Horn holds, indeed, some very strong views on sarcasm—that weapon of the second-rate mind.

With my publishers' permission I will now give a large slice of the story, and those "reactions," written in a letter to them at Christmas (1927) just after the departure of Trader Horn for England and his daughter's home. The letter runs:

"I thought you would like to know something about the last month or three weeks Trader Horn spent before sailing to find his daughter in England.

"As you may remember he spent six months in Durban (April to September, 1927) and then, after a few hectic weeks in Johannesburg, which caused us considerable anxiety for we never knew just where he was and who might be borrowing money or drinks, he suddenly grew tired of Johannesburg and decided to go into the country for a bit, near Pretoria, about fifty miles away.

"There he stayed at the Salvation Army men's home,* and foregathered with various old friends of the early gold-rush days and led a model life for a month. Then he suddenly appeared on our door-step at eight o'clock one fine morning. It was mail day, and an exceptionally busy one as, at the moment of his arrival, I was dictating the last paragraph of Vol. 2 to Dr. Lewis before he went to his laboratory. I also had a mountain of arrears of letters to write, as one usually has after finishing a book. But there was little chance to write them—I have found from long experience that Trader Horn, like the last of the saga tellers, as he is, dominates the house with his reminiscences, and no writing is possible. That is why, after taking notes steadily for fifteen or sixteen months after he first appeared, until I had amassed enough for three volumes, I had at last to get him away from Johannesburg for a long period—not only for him to avoid the cold winter but for me to be able to get under way with Vol. 2.

"It was this same morning on which the letter arrived from his daughter.

"After reading it and growing a bit wet-eyed over it, as even a wild old man might well do, he gave it to me to take indoors and have a good look at the photos. But as I reached the door, he said anxiously:

* I have an interesting and warmly friendly impression of the old man in a letter from Captain Vaughan of the Salvation Army which I hope to publish later.

'You'll give it back to me, won't you? If I like a thing very much I have a habit of wanting to read it twice over.'

"Indeed, he read it many times that first day, and fell asleep in the afternoon with the photos spread all over his chest.

"As I was very busy indeed I went to look for a respectable small hotel nearby where he might stay. We were expecting the painter from England to do his portrait, and I was anxious not to lose sight of the old man for that reason. I found a suitable hotel and paid for his room for a month. My brother, his Rustenbery friend, and myself took him over and installed him, but he was obviously very sad and unwilling to go and be left alone there. When I, in a day or two, discovered the reason I sent a taxi for him and had him come back to our house, bag and baggage (which at that time was a couple of kitbags and some deplorable remnants. But always his prayer book, his American edition of *Trader Horn* and his paintbox).

"The reason was that he was afraid to go on the streets for fear of meeting too many of his old doss-house companions and other possible borrowers and hard drinkers. More than that—his daughter's letter had given him a sort of shock. He realised, at the sight of it, what sort of a life he had been leading. Mentioning one or two of his old companions he said: 'I'll not meet those fellers again. It's too degrading, now I'm a grandfather to those little girls.

When you're a grandfather you've got to be more careful of appearances.'

"So he went very thankful into the little room in which we keep the typewriter and the Encyclopædia Britannica and a camp bed for wayfarers and a 'rhyme-sheet' or two on the walls for cheerfulness, and there he stayed for three weeks—until he left for Cape Town and the *Durham Castle.*

"I believe those three weeks to be the happiest of his life. He was safe, his passage was taken for England, and he had the grandchildren to think about. It was a little harbour before setting sail to a new phase of life.

"After five days or so the portrait painter appeared. During those five days the old man was very busy in the mornings making his Christmas gridirons for me * in the lumber room. Or I gave him an hour or two in which to write autographs or sign books and photos before he went away.

"He loved wandering about the house and garden and not having to say 'au revoir' at the gate as he had done some scores of times when he lived at the doss-house. He loved wandering into the kitchen

* I had suggested that he should make a gridiron as his Christmas gift to our American publishers. He joyfully went to his "old place" to buy the wire and was soon at work. He also, to please me, made one for Pauline Smith's kitchen in her cottage in Dorset. The sight of Zambesi Jack in the streets with a roll of wire gave rise, I believe, to the rumour that he had gone back to his peddling. But it could not have given rise to the news that he was still selling wires on doorsteps and "boasting that he had written a book." It is very probable that he had impersonators here and also in Natal where, long after he had left, I heard that he was going round booking orders for his next book.

when Ruth* was busy with the vegetables or making a pie. He would steal raw peas and carrots or taste the cake just like a boy. He loved the kitchen too when it was cold and would sit by the stove late at night when all was quiet and tidy and no one there. If it rained we had a fire in the sitting-room, as we often do in summer here. And there he would sit and smoke and tell stories until bed time. If he thought we were busy or preoccupied he would go to bed after dinner. But would appear again, fully dressed still, about eleven, have a drink and begin an entirely new sheaf of reminiscences. Until, towards midnight, we had to be very firm and send him back to his bed.

"At these late appearances he would often wear his hat. Twice I came in from the theatre to find my son or my husband entertaining Trader Horn in his hat —in my drawing-room!

"Very often Ruth, on entering her kitchen at 5.30 in the morning would find the old man smoking by the still warm stove still wearing his hat!

" 'I tell him,' Ruth said, 'that an old respectable gentleman like him ought to stay in bed till seven.'

"And he would go meekly back and creep into bed with all his clothes on. And, so Ruth assured me,

* My coloured cook (see *Trader Horn, Volume One*) whose reactions to the Hornbooks are not without interest. For when intimating that she would appreciate a copy of Missis's book in which her name appears she said: "That'll show my people in the country that we don't all go for mischief when we come to Johannesburg. We live respectable and it's time they knew it."

often still wearing his hat; as she discovered when taking him a cup of early coffee.

"So glad was Trader Horn to find sanctuary that in a stay of three weeks he only went outside the gate four or five times. Once it was to buy himself some dried fish with which he guiltily stole into the kitchen and persuaded Ruth to cook. We naturally increased the fish diet after that. Then he went once or twice to mass and once to confession. There was a Catholic Church within a short distance by tram. It was his daughter's letter which appeared to make it necessary for him to go through some spiritual cleansing. In fact, a great change came over him from the day the letter arrived.

"One item of news in the letter was that one of his priest brothers, Father——, had recently died and left his fortune to Chinese Catholic priests. This was a blow and a surprise to Trader Horn. He had been assured that his daughter would inherit her uncle's money or some of it.

"So on the Saturday night after the letter arrived the old man said his thoughts of his brother had been such as made it necessary for him to go and get rid of them in confession. Which he did, and came back as happy as a child.

"My husband and I were sitting on the stoep when he returned. He called out to us eagerly as he mounted the steps one by one that it was 'all right—that priest down there had told him there'll always be room for the wild 'uns up aloft. Always a bit o' love left for the wild lads in the ultimate.'

"It is not the first time Trader Horn has been to confession since I knew him. When first he appeared I asked him if he went to mass still. He sadly intimated that 'things had gone a bit too far for that.' Meaning that he was too great a sinner. However, feeling more optimistic about it than he did, I went to see a priest—who had one of the finest and kindest brogues I ever heard, and is probably a changeling, for he has shuttle-shaped pupils placed perpendicularly in eyes green as a cat's—and within a few weeks Trader Horn had returned to the bosom of his church.

"I must now describe something of the painting of the portrait. The painter arrived one Sunday morning from Durban, and next day was hard at work on a preliminary charcoal sketch. He was extremely grateful to have—on his arrival in a strange city—the immediate privacy and peace of the lumber room. The new and splendid and steady light pouring in from the hole in the roof, the strange old man, the medley of antique and ailing furniture, etc., pushed on one side, all pleased his artistic mind, which is used to the casual caravan life followed by some English artists in the summer.

"Fortunately, Trader Horn at once 'sized up' the artist with approval: 'A nervous feller that. Never still. But goodness writ on a face like that. A gentleman to the bone. Oh, aye, he'll make something out of it. He'll never be content with second best you'll see. A top notcher. But you should see his antics! Like a fencing master the way he lunges about after an idea. He'll walk a thousand miles round that easel before he's done.' The easel, by the way, was a tall stepladder with a ledge nailed across one of the steps.

"Every morning for sixteen days the old man sat for the picture. And the artist thought of nothing but the picture and would continue to get abstractedly lost when, during the afternoon, he went into the streets and suburbs of Johannesburg. Often they sat until it was well on in the afternoon, the artist having a simple lunch of fruit and bread and cheese sent in to him. The old man had determined not to miss the *Durham Castle* and Christmas with his grandchildren. And on that day he left for the docks he sat on until five o'clock. When I suggested to the painter that the old man would be overtired he looked sad. And Trader Horn came into the house and said: 'Don't hurry him. Poor feller, it might be his banner picture, and I'm going to spoil it for him just because of those grandchildren.'

"So the picture grew from the first charcoal sketch which looked just as the Trader might have looked at thirty-five, to be a grey-haired man of sixty. Every day the artist wanted our opinion on the face. We had a long discussion as to wherein lay the greater artistry—in painting a decrepit old man with second childhood artlessly smiling in the background or in making him the Trader Horn of his virile days. It did not take long to realise that stark realism can sometimes be inartistic—can actually convey the wrong impression of character. After all, William Tell on his deathbed would not be the real William Tell: we want to see more than the deathbed can show us—we want to see him in the supreme hour of life. Just as we like to think of Newton staring at the dropped apple. Napoleon at Longwood is no longer Napoleon—he is the sport and plaything of that great feline, time, with the sharp, reminding claws.

"Modern playwrights and authors naturally veer towards cruel realism—but how could one be cruel to the immortal boy that is Trader Horn? Incorrigible at school and incorrigible still; playing in his old age in the corridors of life while others sit dully at their desks for a lifetime. So the painter gives him back a few precious years, and puts a gun in the hand which now can hardly 'twist up' the wire for a gridiron.

"There was trouble about that gun. Of the first one he posed with, he said morosely: 'Oh, aye, it'll *do*. But you couldn't expect me to kill an elephant with it.' Afterwards one of the right period and pattern was brought to him and he grasped it happily as if still a hunter. No, you realists! do not grudge him the gun: not after a record like his. Let him go down to posterity with it, for he has surely earned the right, even as the old vikings were buried with weapon and dog and trusty servant.

"Yes, the man in the portrait is very different from the feeble, quiet old man with the waxen face, the Aloysius of October, 1925.

"And in Trader Horn's face as it is to-day there is substance, healthy tissue and colour. There is even arrogance and not a little bombast when he thinks to himself of some of those fellows at the stock exchange who, in their offices, have occasionally stolen the old prospector's brains for half a crown: expert opinion for which they should have paid a couple of guineas or more: mean fellows. One of these men, a mining expert, even had the cynical effrontery—after success had come to the book—to ring me up and suggest that Aloysius Horn might like to 'go in with him' in some mineral speculation in Angola. I think he hoped by this means to persuade the Trader to eventually go to the spot and point out the place where a vast fortune in copper will one day be made. Rarely has a telephone conversation given me such complete satisfaction as the one I had then.

"I must describe the last two evenings Trader Horn spent with us. On the last but one he refused to go to bed early. He said he was feeling like Christmas; like apple-snatching and the peace egg, same as they had when he was a boy. Wasn't he setting off next day to join his daughter and her children for Christmas? (For the last few days he had arranged a sort of little altar on his dressing-chest; their photos, held in place by his prayer book and festooned about with his rosary of brown beads.) So my husband and I respected his mood and sat up till midnight talking round the table, or rather letting him talk.

"He had for many weeks been thinking of a new story and on this last night we heard all the personal experiences that were the origin of the story. He surpassed himself in picturesque language as he described the caravans coming along in the moonlight along the Lake Chad road with their precious freight of——

"But I must not go further with a story that is still his, not mine. After his departure I found one sheet of the story: he had begun at the end! That is what age does for you, I suppose: so short is the time that you write 'The End' before you dare to inscribe 'Chapter One.' There it was, half a page, embodying the close of the story and then

'The End'

heavily enscrolled by flourishes of the pencil. I stared long at it—the last page of so many left for me in my house, before putting it away with my other notes and MSS.

"This was the night before he left. On the next day I was marking and packing all the new clothes which during a fortnight I had been buying and having made for him: and all the Christmas presents he was taking home to the grandchildren. On this day he received a letter from a female cousin of about his own age of whom he had heard nothing for thirty years or more. She said: 'Do you remember, dear

Cousin Wish, when you were a boy going off to the West Coast, and your mother was getting your outfit ready and we came over to spend the day? And we all prayed for you in the drawing-room?' And here was Aloysius, just fifty years later, having another 'outfit' made for another journey. Markings and packings and excitement. Everything new. As the painter said 'like sending him off to boarding-school.'

"He sat to the painter (fortunately for the packing) until five in the afternoon. His restlessness was complete and contagious, and nothing but the portrait could keep him quiet. The train went at ten o'clock. After dinner, while doing the last few things, such as luggage labels, we had our first serious difference of opinion. It might not have occurred if we had not both been somewhat tired and overwrought after the busy day. It flared up unexpectedly over the wearing of a tie. He suddenly refused to put on a tie: that garment which, old but beautifully tied, he had desperately clung to in his doss-house days (for an old man selling things at doors must look neat and trim) he rebelled against in his hour of opulence. And with all his grand new clothes in his trunk, Trader Horn went off in an old suit of reach-me-downs, and old jersey, and—no tie. He also smuggled—as he fondly imagined till I saw them—some still older, more disreputable clothes into a kitbag. But the steward had his orders—posted a week before. (One was, I remember, to try to persuade Mr. Alfred Smith, under which name he travelled, to wear braces instead of a belt on nearing Tilbury for the sake of the tailor who had done his best to get a cut.) But I feared the worst for my plans when, just before the taxi came, we gave him his money for the voyage and a fine new pocketbook to put it in. He cast a look of scorn on the pocketbook and said deliberately: '*Ikorna* *—pocketbook! Get your needle, ma'am, and sew up this pocket.' As I had not seen or used a needle for months this flurried me considerably at the last moment. However, a needle was found, although not a thimble, and while my husband held up the coat I stitched up the hip pocket into which Mr. Horn had rammed all the notes but three. And then I knew that, steward or no steward officiously valeting him, Trader Horn meant to sleep on his cache throughout the voyage; just as he has in camps and bivouacs all his life."

And now, forgetting pocketbooks and passports, I turn back to that Trader Horn with whom romance has walked so closely; who has always had a nodding acquaintance with the improbable, and about whose person glows too the aura of *coincidence.*

"Nothing to do with romance," says my young daughter flatly; "he's just an old fairy man. Just *look* how he looked when he sat on the edge of the sofa in that farmhouse and didn't say anything. . . . Of course he's an old fairy man."

* A Bantu word expressive of scorn, disbelief or denial.

That is the idea of a girl of sixteen. But I have a woman friend of the mature age of twenty-eight, Winifred Holtby,* herself of wonderfully pure Danish stock from what I privately call "the viking area of Yorkshire." This practical young Oxford woman, with a good history degree, when lecturing in South Africa for the League of Nations, was my guest for three weeks at the time when I was weekly taking down the material for this book. We used to talk over my notes with very great excitement, for she was of the old sea breed herself. And had I not poured into my own first novel, published in London nine months before the old man turned up, my own deep love for the old northern stock from which I also spring?

Too busy with meetings and lectures during the day to have any talk together we used to make midnight feasts in the kitchen and turn the strange happening this way and that to have a good look at it. And this is what Winifred Holtby said more than once: "There's something supernatural in an old man with a viking complex coming to *your* doorstep. Why should he come and babble of vikings to you of all people? It simply is not an ordinary happening that in all this huge country he should find the person most likely to listen to him."

There are other coincidences of which I have made careful note; one was that when his daughter wrote and told me that for about two years now she had felt that her father was on the way I put the dates together

* Author of some good Yorkshire novels.

and saw that she first had those premonitions at the time when her father first walked through our gate.

So, what with one thing and another, I am often inclined to believe in my daughter's simple solution—that Aloysius Horn is just an old fairy man. It would certainly explain the ease with which he captures the strangely fresh and primitive atmosphere of viking days in the earlies.

E. L.

South Africa,
February, 1928.

PROLOGUE

"I COULD be weaving you another book, Ma'am, if it would please you. I miss my old Ivory in the Earlies since I delivered the last instalment. Seems as if I couldn't sleep in the night for thinking what could be done in the way of literature.

"Do you—do you think it will ever get as far as a printer's, that memoir of mine I've given you? Excuse the remark. Well, whether it does or not you've done your best. And it sure is a bit of a rest from life to come here on Mondays and take a literary view. Same as we did at George Bussey's when I was a young feller. This so-called commerce that instructs me to go round selling a toast-fork and so on in the suburbs is apt to mould you into an automaton. No free play of the ideas same as when I was establishing commerce up a wild river.

"Aye, when you've got to assuage a cannibal into the buying mood 'tis a more manly effort than facing a woman who doesn't want to buy. Some of 'em set the dog after you. They don't know I've faced rogue elephants. Lions in sets and so forth. When you've heard the gorillas roar at dawn it takes away the capacity for fearing the common house dog. His bark falls a bit flat to his own ears before he's reached the gate after me. We have a look at each other the woman can't understand. Aye. Dogs . . . Look at the brain-box provided by Nature above the eyes. He gets his instructions from there, not from some ill-educated woman.

"If you'll excuse the suggestion, Ma'am, I've brought with me a couple of pages sampling an idea I had. I couldn't lay claim this time to it being autobiography. Nothing more than ancestry so-called. It's Vikings got into my head. I've been seeing 'em this last week when the light was out. So yesterday when I woke up I got me pencil and wrote this page or two to solidify my notions. If you like it I'll chase the idea into a story. Take it inside, Ma'am, and see what you think of it. But you must bear in mind that this is only the rough thread—it'll be woven out into something shapely if you like the notion. I know you'll help me with some of the fancy parts. High lights and so on. Ladies dresses, and the love-light, if there is any."

I took the two thin sheets of paper and read this:—

Web-feet.

Very many years have passed since the Dawn of History but still when we hear the stories handed through the generations of the doings of our ancestors we always feel interested whilst listening to them Especially to stories of Sea roving of the old bygone days interest those who can lay claim to be born of the same ancestery. In North West Lancashire were the inhabitants can lay claim to be the derect decendants of the old sea rovers or sea vykings there is a special longing for this kind of yarn which is generally doled out during the long winter nights so as to give the rising generation an opportunity to learn the Folk Lore or history of the country they claim as their own.

The following storie is about as near as I can remember of something that happened during the days of Rodger the Bold who had his keeps and castles amongst the Faroe Islands. Rodger had only one son who like his father was born with webbed feet and hands. Children born with webbed feet are said to be lucky I myself had a cousin who could claim to be a lucky member of his family on that account. Here amongst the spume and rolling Surfs of the Faroes young Harrold was reared. The communities were divided into three classes Sea Pirates craftsmen such as ship builders Smiths and other tradesmen Whilst the rest were small farmers. All shared in the common wheal and all were well skilled in the use of Weapons and not only the men but many of the women were hard to beat at strong bow shooting. Wild Animals were plentiful whilst the coast supplied fish and waterfowl in great abundance whilst the farmers were excelent husbandmen so that these old vykings were well supplied with food. Whatever the rovers brought home after their summer foorays were luxeries in clothing Wine and dainties which they plundered from ships on the high seas. The sea they claimed to be their property by birth right. Thus they were a hardy race of people who looked upon roving as an honourable business. And up to the conquest of England which they settled had claimed no land as their own Except what was to be found around their keeps or castles.

"You'd *like* me to go on with it, Ma'am? If you'll excuse me thanking you it does me *good* to bring you a few sheets every Monday! It makes the days go. And a story about Lancashire, Ma'am, and vikings—'twill be easy woven! 'Tis no more than getting your dreams on paper.

"Aye, when they come to this so-called senility a Lancashire man's always something to fall back upon. Not like those English fellers—London and so on. If I am childish it's surely pleasurable to be a child in my own portion of earth, where you could walk blindfold. Aye! Blindfold or not you can hear the gulls at Gillmoss and smell the salty spume in the air. . . .

"That's a sure relief to me that you like it, Ma'am. It'll all come clear in the nights now if I let it. If only the other fellers won't spoil the vision. They don't comprehend that I must light a candle to get it down while it's there. They make me lose hold when they shout at me to put the light out. They think I've had a dream.

"So—it won't be goodbye just yet. Only another spell of au revoir. Aye! If you could spare me some foolscap and a fresh pencil I'll soon be getting into me swing again. . . .

"What's that, Ma'am? Web-foot? Why, sure! Isn't my own cousin, Martin W—— a web-foot? Feet and hands too. That's folklore I'm spinning you but it's true folklore. Never been in a newspaper. It's one of the luckiest things for a Lancashire man to be—webbed like a viking. I know one or two families where there are fine ladies 're webbed too. They can't pull their gloves on properly nor play the piano, but they're grand in the water. Of course they'd not publish abroad that they're webbed ones. It naturally makes a lady sensitive not to be able to play the piano. Aye, they keep it quiet, but the luck of the vikings is surely their's.

"Well then, Ma'am—here's to Au Revoir. And if you like Old English I'll throw you some in. *Plus* tickling the fancy of Lancastrians it'll attract the Americans too. They've always had a fancy for reading about pure English and so on."

CHAPTER I

BOLD RODGER the Vyking was now ready with his fleet of (40 sail) rovers to make his yearly trip. But as was his custom he always held a galla week before parting with his kinsfolk. Whilst the young folk vied in shooting the poppinjay the men had strongbow contests. They were probably the best Marksmen in the world, whilst the arrows they used were over a yard long and some of them were weighted shafts and left the bow at such a speed that should they hit a steel helmet or breast plate were sure to knock the wearer sprawling and out of combat. Whilst a lighter bow was used for shooting sea birds and poping Jays the arrows were smaller and the bows more easy on the jerk. As the bow was used from the earliest youth up and was the main weapon in War and hunting it was wonderful to see how they could split switches and some were so keen eyed they could down a bumble bee at fair distance. This bow shooting was keenly contested and the prizes given to winners were costly and were to be seen displayed each year in the keep. Whilst the looser or worst hindmost archer was always carried to a cliff rock and thrown in the see for a ducking amidst the laughter and mirth of the onlookers. After the day's Sport was over there was always a brewing prize at Roger's keep. The great hall was always crowded, whilst the Ale was handed round in horns for judgement and served by the wenches who were concerned in the making of the brew. The lasses who won the contests in beer and ale making were always in request by wifeseekers, and as the weddings took place on the wind up of the Galla, were generally well wed. The next day of the sports was swimming and diving, water polo, popping the ball and surf riding and as the people were all born by or on the sea it was only the best swimmers who contested. As I before told you, many of the people born in the Keep of the Faroes had web feet and hands and although these were swift divers under water were no better than their kinsmen at battling surf and tipping breakers, but it was there that Rodger's son a well-built lad of sixteen showed up. He was born webbed hand and foot and in the contests won the under-the-water prize by fetching (fetching is the old name for diving) 406 Yards in quick time, veryly a man fish and when he bobbed up, his head on the mark, he dived again and afterwards clombed up the sea stairway smiling and with no wind shortage showing neath his hairy chest on his back coming. This feat was loudly cheered by all the folks who were there and then the chief race of the day, a mile and back through a High sea surf was the next happening. It was heralded by loud blowing of sea horns (concha). And Harold the Webbed was looked upon as a lad with a likely chance to win. The lad was resting from his last effort before climbing the steep rocks and over to the sea, but the lasses came to his aid saying in Old

English If tha can win tha cant win tired out and they gently gripped his thighs and arms and shouldering him with a laugh they raced him down the deep cliffs and dumped him on the surf-pounded Ocean shore near the din of the mighty breaking surf. Two long straight lines had been made in the sand and here were stood in line about 20 men, and many of them were old time veterans at the game of surf dodging. One old man Anlaf the blacksmith was heralded as a sure winner and the next best was called Pated Chuck (old English for Charlie) who was hard to beat. The distance was a Mile each way and was marked by a floating tub with a red flag above it. The starter stood ready with his flag held up. The beach and hillside was crowded as this was looked upon as a great event. The flag was dropped and all the swimmers had disappeared except Anlaf and Chuck who stood watching for the big breakers to roll in; as it thundered on the shore they struck in low on the under tow and on coming up they were way ahead of those who took the surf too high. On turning the buoy Chuck was a good first, Anlaf second nearly tied by young Harold. The loud cheering from cliff and chore could be well heard above the ocean din (Anglo Saxon noise). The rest of the tryers doubled the Buoy at various distances, as the men swam low there was no telling how things were going on in a broken sea. Strained eyes now watched for the winner to come through the surfs. Now the loud cheering started as back they came flashing flashing through like porpoises. Then out of the beach roller popped harrold, then Chuck, then Anlaf the Smith. Harold passed the line first and a yard behind him Chuck while Anlaf was five yards behind him. Such a thing had never happened before, the race had been won by a sixteen year old boy. But wait a While, the fun had not yet started till amidst a peal of laughter in came the last man. And such joking and laughing and shouting you never heard as the wenches grabbed him and dumped him in a canvas held taut by strong armed lasses amongst rock honey and duck feathers and as they yelled and shouted they twitched the canvas keeping time with the old chanty, Muck midding (old English for Ash Tub). The poor fellow was tossed high up and as he lighted first on head and now on tail and now on one side and then on the other he was soon Honey and feather all over. He was then stood up and they pulled a hold of feathers from each eye, another pluck showed his mouth and then his nose was cleaned and as he had a long nose with a red end the wenches and everybody else screamed with laughter. All cried oh what a bonny bird. And as the long Feathers dangled down they told him to beat his wings and as he was enjoying the fun as much as anybody he mimacked flying causing peals of merrie Laughter. He was now presented with a feathered oatcake and let go amidst three cheers. The race was over and All now hurried up the cliff galla mad. The next turns were held in the valley between the hills. This was a famous place and here was held such sports as Battle axe versus sword, tilting on ponies, weight throwing and wrestling. As the weather was fine these sports were daily kept up till the last day of the week the principal day Sunday was as the name indicates a day of sun worship, the day being kept up in those days by getting the full benefit of the sunshine if there was any and was a day of rest and pleasure, when the old ones delighted to ly in the sun shine while the youngsters played around such games as hanball, shuffle-cock, and archery being the principal sport. As Sunday was called prize day the rewards were handed out the castle hall and this being over wedding took place. The girls who had won the Ale and Brewing contests were now offered to gallants. The las who had won first prize had ten offers six of the men were old tho born with good tastes and on being refused caused much merriment amongst the onlookers. The next two were twin brothers and the bonnie lass had no choice but this was soon decided by Old Chief Rodger calling on them to decide by wrestling. This bout was keenly watched as the bout was best two out of three and was won by the smallest twin who was loudly cheered. The harps now filled the hall with joyous music whilst, holding hands the first pair jumped the Besom (Broom). This was followed by several more couples who were showered with flowers and received quite a number of presents and now the dancing began to the music of fiddles and harps. Mean while the smoking bores heads came in without which no galla was ever finished. These with roasts of prime beef and other well-known Tit bits were laid around the hall on long low tabeles filled with new nuts fruits and Honey lolly Pops whilst cheese butter eggs and Victles of all kinds were piled round in plenty. The wine most of which had been looted in the forrays on the sea was also brought up from the cellars and Caves of the castle keep and that with a supply of new and old ale galore was partaken of (as you like) after every dance. It was midnight when the Old Chief smiling largely left the party wishing them the best of these good times, as he was bound out to sea in the early morn and promised to return with his fleet of fourty sail brimfull of loot of the best Quality. He was cheered to the echo on leaving, whilst most of the younger folk kept up the feast and dancing till early morning. Before sunrise the fleet was ready and loosing no time as all Good byes had been said before hand the small boats left the beach with their crews of strong men clad in brown leather and burnished shoulder and breast chain Jackets which glistened in the rising sun whilst on Rodger's copper helmet were two Eagles wings one on each side with a topping of cocks feathers. They were cheered to the echo as they left their moorings one by one in file and looked like white winged birds as they skimmed the Spume and disappeared in the west.

CONVERSATION

"I've brought you the swing-off, Ma'am. It took massive shape two nights ago. I'd got a bit of a chill what with one thing and another. My shirt was wet and there was rain coming in through the window on to the bed and I couldn't lay me hands on anything dry. But I got off to sleep nice and warm after all from the drink Honest John gave me. Him that was the first Jew in Rhodesia and could have been King of the Kalihari if he'd sold a wagon-load of rifles to Swaart-booi. He said to me 'What's the matter, Jack? * You're looking a bit down.' I told him I'd got a chill selling me wires and a sort of a queer pain in me chest to the left here, ma'am. So he gave me a tot and I went straight to my room. I'm not generally drinking with Israel, but John has the gift of universal bravery—makes him somewhat more than Jew. 'Tis with the man I drink, not the Jew.

"Aye, the rain was beating in, but when I woke up I felt warm and lively and I seemed to see the thrushes hopping about the lawn like when I slept at Frea. Sort of attic window we had, and we could stand outside it on a little ledge where the window went into the roof. I doubt I was a bit lightheaded from the chill. I must 'a got thinking of all the stories woven to us when we were little lads. All at once I saw Cæsar's fleet and all its fancy regalia bright in the sun, and I saw that young lad o' sixteen with his ringlets shining like white silk, and I jumped out o' bed chill and all and seized me pencil and paper.

"Ma'am, it seemed as if I'd been waiting all me life to set down what's in the heart and bones of Lancashire men. Proper folk lore, that was told to my uncles and my grandfather when they were young lads same as it

* Zambesi Jack, Mr. Horn's name amongst the old-timers.

was to me. Aye, I couldn't stop the furore until I saw the picture coming clear under me hand.

"Nice visions of Fingall's cavern I've been having. I used to go swimming near Fingall's cavern with H—— D——, my cousin. We could get through surf that no nigger could touch. Swimming's always been a bit of a blot on Africa. No native is *au fait* with the waves as we are. Aye, 'twas going out with H—— brought the idea. That's where I copped it.

"Fingall's cave, with the great gates of copper that'll be let down to keep the ships out, and a smooth inland sea inside, with room for thirty sail. A big, extensive, natural store. Aye, you can see the lads going up the great stairway of stone from the cave. All in the torch-light and staring round at the foreign gewgaws when they come to the big hall where Chief Fingall sits with his girls. Fine daughters he had. They stared at each other long enough, all being youngsters. And Harold with his webs all sandy and his ringlets like wet silk from the sea water.

"They thought that naked lad must have come through the surf, from Hades or through the Styx. Or maybe a water-blarney. He'd be naked, but give him skintights for the susceptibilities.

"Ma'am? Well, a water fairy, of course. Tommy Bamber had a peculiar knowledge *re* old English. And there's a bit for yer.

"No, I can't say what they do in Ireland beyond the portals of Fingall, paramount chief of the north. Blarney stone? Well, of course it means fairy stone.

What else? A word they've looted from the old English. Words got spread about more easy than you'd think, with forays and the looting of women and slaves as hostages. The poor things'd surely remember a little word like blarney.

"Well, now, I shall be O. K. with the lot. The first chapter's always the critical period, George used to say. No need to begin with a learned history of the vikings Macaulay's style. Make one of 'em live and you sense the lot. You'll see 'em at their daily life, laughing and playing. A feller can't always be standing on the prow of his ship like in these cinemas.

"Excuse me, ma'am—I'll excuse you if you take it inside and leave me for a bit. I've plenty to meditate over. This sun sure invites pleasurable fancies. Aye, there's something in a garden provides peace. Yes, I've got me pipe but I'm wanting you to cast an eye on what I've given you. Never mind me—you must excuse me if I hurry you about like a daughter sometimes. I forget. . . ."

"There you are, ma'am. You've been very quick. Did you *get* it all? How do you think it rings for a start? Those games provide a fine panorama of natural amusements in the earlies. Makes a bright opening writers'd call topical. On the eve of action. If I were to bring in the games last of all 'twould fall somewhat flat after such a spectacle as I'm going to summon up of the dawn-light of England. 'Twould never do to let the domestic follow the warlike. But if we run the domestic in now, you're in the story, amongst the folk, before you know where you are.

"I thought to meself I must give 'em a smack of old English in this book. Aye, we must give it a smack! I know old English, and I'll throw you in lots of words, ma'am, 'll please the literary. Folk lore, too. The folk lore of a sensible fighting people is always of value to the world. And there's nobody to gainsay it now. In the archives, perhaps; but they won't speak. They're dumb except to learned scholars like Lingard—could read 'em easy as a newspaper.

"Folk lore. We lads in Lancashire used to listen to all the bold stories on winter nights when Tommy Bamber was rife. Illustrious Tommy Bamber—him that saw the fight off Galveston! Aye, lads are the ones to listen! Same as these boys I'm going to throw into the story. *I'm going to make 'em truants.* How does that strike you, ma'am? Steal their father's ship and go off on a foray for loot. A lad doesn't find his feet until he runs away at the call of adventure. And when they're left with the women and the wisemen there's nothing tickles a lad's fancy like disobedience.

"I'll—I'll take 'em to see old Chief Fingall, paramount chief of the North of Ireland in those days. That'll be a novelty. I know the Yankees, ma'am. North and South I know them, and if you'll excuse me I should say—let's give 'em a novelty plus a bit of instruction. Aye, that's what'll make the book go! Instruction. And something that the young boys and the old men too will like to read. It'll sure tickle 'em to think of those big boys going off with their father's vessel. That'll give 'em a laugh plus the instruction I shall weave into the yarn.

"Aye, and there's a bigger laugh to come. What do you say to the apparition of these truant boys of the north boarding their own father's vessel by mistake in the thick dew? * Grappling before they knew where they are! Going to loot their own sire and other notable vikings of the day. Aye, if it's a laughable interlude you want, that'll make a pretty comedy of errors. You can sell it to these so-called cinema experts if only they didn't ruin good history with a massive ignorance.

"Look at that feller that's doing 'The Sea Hawk.' [Some one had treated Mr. Horn to an evening at the pictures.] Very meagre ideas. No *mélange,* as the French say. If you were to ask me, I should say it's because it hasn't got the refining influence of history at the back of it. You've got to stiffen out a flimsy notion with the truth as it has come down to us in history. You can't get reality out of a few feathered hats, trunk hose and so forth. Elizabethan times had a few more truisms [*i. e.,* realities] in them than could be found in the wardrobe of a fancy fop like Darnley—Elizabeth's paramour, that's the feller I'm talking about.

"Aye, she married him off to that poor girl Queen Mary so that she could keep him in the family with less scandal to herself. A noted apostate, that woman! Wanted to keep him as her lover while still retaining the title of Virgin Queen.

* Fog.

"Come to lovers: Mary was none too choicey either. She got herself stolen once by a freebooter called Bosworth. Begged for it. When out hunting near the old Trough o' Bolland and got herself lost in the woods on purpose. Aye, she picked up this ringletted freebooter easy as if he'd been royalty. They lived at Bosworth Keep, defying Elizabeth. He had his brigands there as garrison. The Virgin Queen was naturally irritable at the spectacle of her cousin's popularity with the opposite sex.

"If at any time you think of writing on the subject you could easy weave that into the history of Mary Queen of Scots. 'Sidelights on the Scottish Queen,' it could be called. Better draw in a bit of folk lore, et cetera, for stability's sake.

"Know a good deal of history? Why, ma'am, I was born where it's made. There's more truisms in Lancashire than the metropolis itself could offer. And what I tell you is not only novelties. There's likely to be a good deal of truth in it.

"Well, ma'am, I've told you my notions *re* the plot, but I mustn't let them gallop me ahead too much or the furore'll leave me before I get there."

(This is exactly what happens to Mr. Horn. The wonder is that, writing where he does, so much furore should remain.)

"If you'll excuse me, ma'am, I'm somewhat fatigued. I'll be getting along before the shower breaks over me. I'm not wanting my shirt wet again."

CHAPTER II

THERE were many eayes strained over the sea to the point in the West where the last ship had disappeared. The boys especially longed to be with their fathers and relatives on this occasion as there must be big happenings somewhere to cause old Chief Roger to light out with forty sail in fact the Pick of his fighting craft. The sea boats left were those specially built for seal and whale fishing and some of these vessels had already reached Green land and probably Labrador and even as far south as the land we now call Newfoundland. In fact we are certain of that as many sea lion tusks are still to be found amongst the Curios to be seen amongst the very old families there whilst many of their boats and ships have been found in the wreckage along the northern coast of the U. S. A. After sailing due west for some time the fleet still sailing in File veered south west and widened their distance between each other and thus had a greater cignalling distance as the large Sea horns could be heard easily for a mile on the water and were easily audoble along the whole line when blown from the last ship by the commander of the fleet. He kept up a communication if necessary along the whole line and the horn was blown across the waters like making pleasant music as the sounds were sent in different Notes all having their meanings and were well understood by those ancient Sea wolves, as they had heard them from their childhood up. The direction they had now taken was the course by which they would eventually arrive at Fingall's country in the north west of Ireland. Fingall at this time was a very powerful chief and not only owned the lion's Share of the north of Ireland but also laid claim to a large portion of the western islands and the costal front of the west of Scotland although his power in this country was often disputed by roving bands from the interior who were a very savage and warlike race and only acknowledged as their frontier border those countries who were able to defend themselves against their frequent attacks. The inhabitants of the islands who were under the rule of Fingall were loud in their complaints of late as they had suffered greatly at the hands of these bands of roving Picts and Scots who had commenced to plunder the small villages and had also carried off some of their young women who were daily engaged fishing along the coast. Bold Rodger the Vyking managed to reach Fingall's coast about dusk and, after horn-blowing and signalling with their horn lanthorns they were at last signalled by the watchers of Fingall's keep. Boats soon put off from the shore and the Viking Chief accompanied by many of his old captains were soon seated in Fingall's great hall which was situated high above the great keep. Here they had a great welcome and after they had drunk a loving cup from the large bowl of Silver handed round by two bearers were soon listening to the news of the hour although the most important matters Fingall left till the early morrow when there would be a gathering of the chiefs. They all slept in the big Hall on Bearskins and other choice rugs and Fingall bidding them good-night retired. Meanwhile in the valley west of the keep were rows of skin tents stretched like Indian Teppes whilst the Irish bagpipes played music to the wild dances of Fingall's men who were making merrie before embarking on their Punative expeditions. Some of these men had come from away off in Fingall's land, and were renowned for their fighting qualities as well as their savage leaders. These were picked troops and many of them were old seasoned fighters who had never suffered defeat. The night was spent in merry-making. King Fingall was early up well before sunrise whilst everything was made ready for the voyage to the Scottish coast. Fingall lost no time but was busily engaged imparting the news of the approach of Julius Ceasar, and as they were no doubt to conquer as much of Britain as was possible and were well equipped and backed by the whole Roman Empire which embraced nearly the whole of the Known World they were an enemy to be reconed dangerous if not checked by the unity of the northern chiefs whom Fingall intended should join a pact for mutual defence. To this Harrold and his chiefs agreed but as the Sismacs or Saxons wanted no lands they would join a pact with Fingall as long as he was willing to agree to their rights to the Sea. This pact was drawn up by Fingall's sages and afterwards was witnessed and signed by the Angles by striking a wax-covered paparus document, each chief did this by thumping on the wax with his fist and these impressions on wax remained sacred for all time. The ceremony was now ended. The Irish chiefs were next called in and received their instructions from their king. The whole force was under the orders of Fingalls fighting general, who was also named Fingall and was a cousin of the kings. Towards evening all the fleet was drawn up ready to receive the small Gallic army and on the word of command they marched to the shore and were conveyed on board by long boats. Many ladies had now entered the great Hall and were a most impressive sight as they formed a most pleasing Contrast to their chiefs who were skin clad and many of them wore their crude crests of beaten mettal which were worked on their round shields. All adieus were short and sweet and amongst great cheers each led out his regiment of warriors fine brawny men whose features were as wild as their trappings whilst their long rover hair formed a wonderful contrast to the light-headed Saxons many of whom wore their hair in braided ringlets. The little army was certainly made up of the best the country could afford, this was shown not only by their build and carriage but the martial way they marched southward amidst the din of the Irish pipes of old Fingall. Twas about sundown when the departure was made. The fleet now increased by six of Fingalls transports sailed mainly due east in the shape of a crescent, and being luckily favoured by the wind arrived in sight of the Islands, and changed its formation into three files followed by the transports. The morning dew was heavy and hung like a blanket and well did it serve the purpose of the invaders who arrived on the Scottish coast unobserved and, quickly as could be Fingalls army made an attack on a large stronghold, the castle of Calhoon. The owner was luckily away with most of his clan and the castle was surrounded at once, and being called on to surrender demanded a parley as the garrison was too small to resist the attack of the invaders for long as they were poorly supplied and were completely Surprised by the attack. Fingall here promised them that if they immediately surrendered and agreed to give up the stolen women he would make no trouble and would harm no one. To this they gladly consented as they were many of the sub-chiefs and garrison who were well tired of the tyrant Calhoun who ruled all with an iron hand. The drawbridge was slowly lowered and Fingalls general entered and was welcomed by all even by the young and beautiful wife of Calhoun. The captured women then in the stronghold were brought forward and handed over, but the sixth wench was missing having fallen an easy mark to Calhouns love-making and had willingly accompanied him on his raid to the south. Here Fingalls general left a garrison quite strong enough to hold the place and was about to attack the other smaller keeps but was held back by a messenjer on the early morn by sad news of the happenings of the night. Now Calhoun hearing of the capture of his keep when he was about thirty miles away rode with all haste to a wood close to the stronghold and sending a messenger who was glib of tongue to the castle, he had bid him to tell his young wife to come secretly to the rock near the road through the forest where he was waiting with his horse. No sooner did the broken-hearted wife hear this and knowing she had been jiltered she determined on revenge. Secretly passing over the open drawbridge, where she was not even challenged as she was known on account of her great Beauty she was full of hate against this false chief but hastening to where he was she carressed him with a smile. He mounted and drew her up to the saddle behind him. He had not ridden half a mile when his wife swiftly drew a dirk and stabbed him in the back. He fell to earth immediately without a grone, mortally wounded. Whilst his wife, grabbing the reins turned and glancing at her dead husband with eyes glinting with fiery hate she said, Let the grey wolves be thy company to-night. There are many here and thou wast always fond of strange company in thy nights rest. This woman, so the story goes, made good her Escape back to her fathers castle in the North from which she had been stolen. On hearing the news the whole of the country which had been dominated by the hated Calhoun came in and surrendered even to the last of command. There was great rejoicing in the land and before nightfall the green flag of Fingall floated supreme through the Islands and shorelands of the west of Old Scotia. There was great rejoicing amongst dwellers on the coastlands, who were tired of constant raids and turmoil. Sufficient troops were left in the keeps for the defence of the country and sweet peace once more reigned over the land. Leaving the garrison behind and all at piece the good fleet sailed back to Fingalls country. On hearing the glad news there were several days of rejoicing and galla and all took part in the sports and pastimes. Fingalls queen when she heard of the glad happenings declared that the hatred of a jiltered woman was far stronger than an army as events had proved it so, and even to our times the country folks speak of ghosts and hopgoblins that loited at night round the stone where Calhoun fell.

CONVERSATION

"I've not had too literary an atmosphere this week, ma'am. They'll put any junk or wayfarer seemingly into my room. It's against the contract, but Israel's apt at not keeping the given word.

"Aye, some of these fellers they give me . . . you can always see when the stamp of Cain's on a feller's physiognomy. The only way you can approach him is to get to his level. There's no redemption for him. Pretty-looking lads some of them! But I have to sleep on my overcoat to keep it these cold days.

"This demimonde—you can get a proper study of it each week in our house. A drinking doctor and a lost lawyer this minute. Last week 'twas the army honoured us. Then there's a traveller comes in sometimes. He makes good money, but he can't stand prosperity. Sold two thousand yards of silk one day, but the commission was too much emotion for him. Foolishly inebriated he gets. You've got to have breeding not to be silly under the circumstances. Aye, you get the full stature of the city, down as well as up, living in a place like that. Yesterday I had to lend me pipe to a bricklayer. Last week it was this barrister feller looked so wretched I had to encourage him with a cup of tea.

"There's great status in having my own stove in my room. Hospitality gives a man self-respect.

"Well, ma'am, the story of these truant Norse lads is sure going to be painted against a background of veritable history. I'm keeping the high lights subdued for a bit. It was an axiom of George Bussey's that it depends where a light is placed whether it's to be effective or not. No need to rush into dramatic panoramas at the offset. Keep 'em in solution to lend colour to the whole. And that's what I'm doing. So here's a chapter of notable sobriety after the carousals of the people in the last one. Chief's in conference and so on. Documents and treaties signed. Not historical enough to be in the archives, but facts that did occur. There's more truisms in Lancashire history than in all England.

[Mr. Horn means truth when he says truisms.]

"Aye, told me by my old uncles same as they told me stories from the Book of Days. Old Mother Hubbard and all these nursery rhymes, they used to know the secret historical meaning of what's only a harmless ditty for a child now. These so-called cartoons—they're nothing for moulding history like a bit of a rhyme that flashes like a fire signal over the country. Imagination is always more stirred by the ear than by the eye. Look at the sea-horn. Called *concha* by the Latins, but I'll have no foreign words in my story! Plain sea-horn is good enough for one of my family. Keyed in three notes according to the signal to be made, and the sound travelling thirty miles over the waves. Aye, when they called to battle 'twas the same for a Lancashire-born as when the Scotch invite the bloodlust with the bagpipes. But not so barbarous. 'Tis a poetic voice crying over the ocean, wild but pleasant, not like these uncouth sirens of the so-called age of steam.

"Aye, when your ship's under steam, and you've got to cry out the news with steam, where's your partnership with nature? Where's the strong ocean breezes to join forces with man if not in filling out his sails and being pressed with bellows into the sea-horn by hearty fellers out for foray? Man's safer when he's a child of nature. 'Tis when he thinks he knows best the trouble comes. Aye, for fellers like me civilization's been nothing but a mishap.

"Well, ma'am, see how it strikes you now. You may find a natural portion of egotism about it but I think you'll find it good. I got a good incentive to twist this Calhoun into it. It makes a fine picture of legendary times that were true. Aye, he lifted her behind him and she clips him loving round the waist. Terrible, the fierce conceptions of a jealous woman! She looks down from the saddle after she has planted the dirk and says: 'Thee was always fond of fresh company in thy bed. Now thee shall have thy fill of it. Aye, the wolves this night shall play with thy fine body, husband.' Bitter as ice she was! The Lancashire folks still keep a good circle away from the place where he fell. Nothing but thistles will ever grow from that bloodstained ground.

"Aye, Lancashire folk have always maintained their folk lore. They'll believe folk lore before they'll believe church. What's bred in the blood can easy oust any information that comes in at the ear.

"Without insulting the mind, excuse me, capturing women in those days was no more than a gentleman attending his office. Robbery was a virtue because it was a livelihood. As it is to-day—look at the statue to Jack Dallas, the biggest freebooter the world has ever known. Tommy Bamber was a great authority on sea fighting and all other freebootery. He'd been with Jack Dallas of Texas.

"Illustrious Tommy Bamber! A beard to his waist and white buckskin breeches.

"Texas, so-called 'the Lone Star State.' Who'd ever think that that pretty name might never have been without the intervention of Providence. Provided two Liverpool men to battle out for possession of a grand bit of country. Jack Dallas and Bill Austin by name. They got out an army of three hundred Liverpool stiffs like themselves, seasoned fighters of fortune. Landed 'em at New Orleans. Water Street, New Orleans. Drilled the army in an upper room in an hotel and sent 'em off to the little republics [?] for soldiers of fortune. They got a hundred dollars each as a start.

"Aye, Tommy Bamber knew a lot about American history.

" 'Twas from New Orleans I left when the big scrap came on. Joined at Savannah with a lot of other old-timers. The *Rochdale* she was called. I'd been travelling as bo'sun from another port. Cargo of sugar we carried, and bound for Hastings. They brought us champagne. We were all oldish men. Aye, we could feel the Southern sympathy.

"The South's always made a feller feel like a gentleman. No gentleman ever needs to hustle. Pretty place, New Orleans! The old French market provides the best cup of coffee in the world. Essentially a French country—the land divided into church parishes. Catholicism grows prettily there. Something spontaneous about it. You'll see the bell ringing even when there isn't a priest. 'Tis some decent soul saying a prayer and touching the bell for piety. Earnest as children about it. Like my Pangwes.

"And who's to say that the Great Onlooker doesn't love us best as children, same as parents do. Same as my daughter cared for Sandy. I lost Sandy once. Shepherd's Bush it was. And that's a thing no mother could forgive lightly. . . .

"In the metropolis, too. Aye—if I hadn't lost Sandy. . . .

"The Redeemer said 'Suffer the children to come to me'. That's plain enough. It's children He wants. He's not asking for Unitarians and other fancy religioners to be brought, arguing their case and so on. Learned talk tires in the ultimate. No love about it. (Excuse me, I know you're Protestant.)

"Aye, that bell, touched by a simple soul. A child pulling at its father's coat—what argument has he but his helplessness? All he's looking for is a clasp of a hand. And that's what you surely find in the older church. Very suitable for an old-timer like me. . . . What accommodation for the old is there elsewhere? And if I'm childish, as I used to suspect, there's no one'll laugh at me there where we've all got to be children.

"Aye, the South. . . .

"The Arkansas rose and swept the levees and we jumped on a passenger train for safety. No need to hide in the blind baggage. With the river rising there was no one with the heart to turn us off. 'Twas a nice interference of Providence. We'd been accused of stealing a nigger's fish from a net. Then some feller from nowhere arrives with a shotgun. Half-French Creoles. Ran us in for theft. They clapped their hands to begin a trial. Aye, when the so-styled judge began to talk he'd only the *patois* to express his feelings. Mine was the French, and it sure cowed him a bit to hear French he couldn't understand.

"I like that Southern country. Pretty old houses. . . . A romantic place, what with the sun and the sea and the bells of the churches.

" 'Twas there I saw an Irishman in a peculiar position. He was a bricklayer and nearing the top of a very tall chimney. He asked for a box to be sent up the scaffold—wanted to stand on it. When it got up there the box was a beehive, taken by misadventure. They got out. In a fine wax they were. I felt sorry for the feller.

"Always a lot o' work for bricklayers in the States. Places grow quickly. Look at Rest Hook [?]! Joseph Hughes found coal at Rest Hook. And Gibsonite, a species of tar. And now it's got barrel factories. Banks and automobiles, et cetera. A big place now. Yes, the bricklayers are always throng in the States, even if it's only on mash-tubs for moonshine.

"I was making mash-tubs meself once up near Blaauw[?]. I was in the X—— Detective Agency at the moment. Duty took me amongst the moonshiners. I had to shadow a feller——

"You're wanted at the gate, ma'am. Poor feller looking for work. . . .

"I thought you'd appreciate that bit about the pact with the Northern chiefs. I've given you a picture of ancient customs there. 'Given under my hand and seal.' The chief's hand smitten on the wax. No gentleman would 'a dared to be able to write in those days. You were classed as a villain if you could write. Knowledge was reckoned a drawback to full manhood.

"The hand on the seal in wax. Aye, no words—for a man! Leave words to the clerks and wisemen. Experts like Lingard know the handprints of the old chiefs. The premier historian of England, his learning comes natural to him. The River Lune flowed past his house in Lancashire where he kept his archives and documents and so on. Aye, flowing under all those ancient bridges, that water could surely 'a given him some exclusive information about Lancastrian history.

"Rivers . . . to me, ma'am, that's known an ancient waterway like the Lune and a wild stream like my Muni River coming from the heights of the unknown, there's something *stultus* in the rivers of South Africa. Something barbaric about a dry riverbed spanned with half a million pounds' worth of machinery. And those rivers'll get drier instead of wetter. Back to barbarity where there's no water. Doesn't all civilization flow from the north where water is? Does the River Lune ever dry up? No, it'll be faithful to Lancastrians for all time. No devils laughing there on the banks, same as they do here. Laughing at the spectacle of bridges over a dry bed.

"Those old stone bridges over the Lune are built of the veritable stones of history. Nobody'll ever mock an old Lancashire bridge that's been doing its duty since the days o' John o' Gaunt. There used to be a bridge near Frea—had the old fist and spear blazoned on it in carving.

"Aye, the Horns—they had the rights of the foreshore from —— to ——. Rights o' piracy, rights o' foreshore, and a fifth to the Queen. That's how it ran. Elizabeth sure had a gift for piracy, whatever her faults. But it wasn't very palatable for an old Catholic family to give up a fifth of what they'd lawfully seized from the sea to one of the newer church.

"Rights o' piracy, rights o' foreshore. . . . Aye!

"Well, ma'am, when I come to the weaving of it I shall be giving you an audacious conception came to me yesterday morning when I woke up. I can think of things before the other fellers wake up and the Golden City begins to shout at you. Ma'am, *those lads are going to see Cæsar!* I'll run 'em down the coast of Wales after they've paid their adieus to Chief Fingall. I know that coast well. Some of the lads at St. Edward's had guardians who took 'em yachting down the Welsh coast and they'd take several schoolfellows for natural company. And down towards the south of England they're going to run into a sight'd glorify the eyes of any lad. 'Tis the spectacle of Julius Cæsar invading Britain! All round about the south coast they see fellers rushing to the shore in their chariots of copper and the great scythes glittering round, with the wheels and the horses lashed to a cruel lather. And they run the boat into a quiet cove and run up the nearest high hill to get a lookout. And when they got to the top it was fuller dawn and they saw the glory and glitter of Cæsar's fleet shining in the sun all S.P.Q.R. Red sails and tinsel and the shining centurions. . . .

"Aye, a heartening spectacle of man power! . . .

"Well, ma'am, I mustn't keep you listening to my ideas. But it does me good to paint it out for you a bit beforehand in lieu of making notes and queries on paper same as George Bussey did.

"This story'll make the most amusing fact. Literature plus folk lore is always liable to attract. Look at the spectacle I'm going to make of the heavy-armoured centurions swept off their feet by arrows from the yards! They could never expect organised warfare from such a primitive enemy. Luxurious armour and the latest fancy notions of science, such as the catapult, have no chance against a man and his bow. *He's mobile.*

"Aye, mobile. And his brains at work. Where's the brain in the catapult? Come to that, where's the brain in heavy artillery? The last man on earth'll be the feller that's saved himself with an arrow. And for close quarters his cutlass or his wrestling prowess.

"Wrestling's always the resource of a strong man. I used to be top of it meself when I was a lad. Like me uncle Eustace. The world's best shot and a great six feet three. A champion wrestler until he killed his brother Aidan with it—and he never used his unruly muscles again.

"A quiet man when I was old enough to know him. But he liked me. The others were always giving him too much advice. All me uncles and aunts. . . .

"Aye, he liked to talk about foreign parts. Wistful he was that he was too late to take a turn for himself across the world. All his strength wasted in staying at home. Never worked at anything in his life—only shooting and hunting. But when he was an old man near to eighty he could take a withy stick thick as my wrist and break it.

"Aye, he became a recluse after killing his brother. They'd been thick as thieves when they were lads, and he never got over it. Wrestling for the championship when they were young fellers, and one day when they were practising for the event he broke his brother's back. He ran for his father to come and see what was the matter. 'Oh, dad,' he says, 'I've hurt Aidan.' They picked the boy up and took him to the house. He didn't last long. 'Dad,' he says, 'I'm going. 'Twas only play, but we were a bit rough.'

"The lad that was left became a recluse, as they say. Meaning the old English word 'mope.' Aye, they couldn't rouse him to a natural life after that. He carried his great strength as if it were a burden to him. Never laughed. But he liked to listen to me when he was getting old.

"Aye, wrestling makes you good friends with a feller. But if you're gifted with muscles above the commonplace you've got to hold back your strength. Keep it in solution. No sudden twists. 'Tis more of a gentleman's exercise than boxing. Less brutality about it, although not so spectacular to the eyes of *Homo stultus*. Doesn't rouse the bloodlust, so-called.

"The last feller in England'll be a wrestler. Some feller with a bow and arrow, plus the muscles of a wrestler. And if he gets blotted out with some flying feller dropping bombs, he'll at least have died like a gentleman. Which is what no bomb-dropper could be. The last on earth, and most likely on Lancashire soil.

"Aye! When the millennium comes, then flying will be a gentleman's pursuit. Pure wanderlust, same as the feelings'll take the ocean eagle from the Cameroons to the Andes every year. And from the Andes to Borneo. And then he scents home again across the Indian Ocean. Thus proving in a few months what it took the world of science some thousands of years to notice—that the world is a sphere.

"Aye, and sleeping on the wing while he's teaching the scientifics. Nature his only god, and he trusts her to guide him while he takes his rest in the air. Like feathered sails, and he drops his weight between them and sleeps sound.

"There's friendship [affinity] between a man and a bird. 'Tis the same instinct forces a lad to a sailing-ship starts the ocean eagle on his travels. They're both looking for a breeze to help 'em elsewhere. Taught by nature herself that permanence is a myth.

"Aye, it's sails does it. Whether in bird life or human a man's *stultus* that can't use a breeze when one comes along.

"Did you know, ma'am, that a ship asks for the best? There's nothing looks so rich about a ship as to have her sails of silk. Like robing a queen, she must have the best and she'll walk the better for it. She surely pays for finery. You can get more out of a ship under silk than under sailcloth. Less bulky. You can crowd more on and less liable to tear. 'Tis breed tells in fabric as in all else.

"I bought the lovely sails of *Shamrock II.* once in

New York. For a new clipper I'd bought for my son. We lost her going up the Delaware. Got into the ice. Just at the spot where Washington crossed.

"Aye, there's flotsam o' mine all about the world. That boat with her silken sails. And that lad o' mine! . . .

"Mesopotamia. There's always something you're never armed against.

"Well, ma'am, I must be trudging along. I haven't been given my wings yet. Excuse me keeping you idle so long."

CHAPTER III

WHILST the merrement at Chief Fingalls was at its height Bold Rodger the Vyking and his captains held continual meetings and made up plans for the future defence of Scotland and Ireland. As the Brittons were too politically divided to be ever united and would no doubt remain so, giving the Romans every chance to over run them, which would never have taken place had the Cambrians and the fierce tribes in North Britain been friendly to each other. Whilst Fingall and the Scotch chiefs although they had old scores to pay off mostly through raiding and women-stealing which was very common at that time but which latter evil as Fingall put it was more a benefit than a curse as it tended to bring new Blood amongst the northern tribes agreed to put away old hatreds and fight for the common wheal. And Rodger even agreed if necessary to raise the tribes of South Iceland and those of the Fyords of Norway, so that the Romans would never be able to land an army only in that portion of South Britain opposite the French coast and this more than proved true in the following years. News had now arrived that a large fleet of galleys and transports had reached the French coast from Rome. So this put an end to further talk, and the Allies being cheered by the glad news made their good buys and boarded their

Ships and put to sea in line at once. They were an imposing sight when viewed from the cliffs of Fingalls keep and as they sailed away like sea birds King Fingall remarked: When those old sea wolves fang on to Seasars ribbs twill surely test the inner metal of this haughty Roman, and I feel content he will return from whence he comes with a sad heart for the ruling of our seas. And now all Fingall Land was aroused, and troops stood ready all through the land whilst down the coast strong patrolls kept continuous Watch by day and night, as Fingall was the last man in the world to be taken by surprise especially as the North was now aroused by what they had heard of the Romans led by Ceasar.

Now let us go back to Rogers home in the Faroe Islands. Whilst their chief was away scowering the high seas in quest of loot on the inner shore we find young Harold sitting amongst a groop of the elderly boys who were full of wanderlust. And one tall lad now stands and throws out the challenge: Make up your minds aye or no. The last to say Aye was the webbed one although he was sick at heart and longed to see the world and especially as some of the boys had been to sea, and one was a navigators son who was quick of ear and sight and new the signs denoted by the sun moon and stars. So without more to do they made ready for the trip choosing a ship which had made a trip to the Greenland coast and had weathered the heavy seas of the far north like a gull and had the name of being the speediest of all afloat. This they provisioned and full rigged, with boarding tacckle, not forgetting arrows and strong bows and all arms needed for looting and telling their mothers they were only going sailing along the Islands for a few days as was their wont, they put to sea. And sailing west they were soon bowling like a greyhound following the course taken by Old Rodger towards the land of Fingall. Harold the Webbed was chosen Chief whilst the long-haired son of a ship builder who had been thrice in foorays with his father named Bill O'Gaunt was welcomed as Young Harold's first mate, whilst the young navigator Kien-of-Eye-and-Ear was acclaimed ships Overseer, not as meant by an overseer of to-day but climed the mast and sitting aloft gave not only ships way but also kept an eye open for quarry. And they bowled along the wavetops like a stormey petrell, which with open wings hits the high spots of the ocean only with his webbed feet, and beak bent on pinching his dinner from the Brine. The crew of twenty was now made into watches and whilst those on first watch were busy making all ship-shape the others willed away the time with tune of harp and merrymaking whilst others crawled forward and took sleep and rest and thus they journied till one early morn a call of Land Ahoi awakened all. The land that showed up in the early dawn was south of Fingalls so said the overseer and from the peak he could well see it was a market day as folks were busy bartering on the shore. So they steered due east lest they might be seen and in the early morn before cockcrow and the first breading sea bird puts out to sea we will, they said, hug the coast before the rising of the dew and get away before the village is awake with such plunder as we can. This coast is the one from which comes fine lace and linnins and homespuns the finest of their kind such as our women like and light to handle I know where off I speak for both my father and I'v looted them before. And thus spake the son of Bill O'Gaunt whom all abord proclaimed to have spoken quite right. And sailing east they made their plans to attack the place on the morrow using the greatest stelth and all were in high glee and they all bent too and made all ready for the dearing do. The night was spent anchored at easy distance from the coast and sails were furled so as to give no passing ship, should they be seen, any inclin who or what they were. They all slept Soundly that were not on watch and dreamed of stack of laces and fine cloths till the hungry sea mews flying from Shorewards awoke them to action. Quickly they bent sail and made towards the beach to a spot selected the day before where the shore was lined by tall trees. When young Harrold according to a plan agreed on by all quietly dived into the sea and was through the surf and crept cautiously up the beach being nearly naked wearing only skin tights, he easily made good his landing, but that was on a spot that was guarded by a knot of watchers who did not tarry a moment but being full of the superstition of their time made fast their escape in the dusk and mist, believing this to be a sea gobling or some uncanny thing they had witnessed as they said when reporting to the shore patroll who were not far distant. At this young Harrold laughed, as he was sure he could regain the sea as he was fleet of foot he crept cautiously towards the town and made sure of his plan of attack, as he could see a short distance ahead small piles of goods around which the men and villagers lay seemingly asleep. And returning still on all fours shorewards to give the happy news to his waiting shipmates on bord his good ship Walrus ready for the fray. But now something stood up before him, and instead of running shorewards he ran with all his might into their center, and although he downed the foremost of them his chance of escape was over as he was set upon and overpowered by a Band of strong armed men and tied hand and foot with thongs and carried to a large hamlet which proved to be the house of Fingalls eldest daughter, and there by the light of torches was examined. He had webbed feet and hands and furthermore bore tatoo marks on his arms. And to the questions asked proved to be quite dumb. At first the onlookers seemed afraid, and questioning him in Gallic asked him if he hailed from Roame or was he fish or man. But Harrold Only smiled, his luck was out and he would no doubt be done to death or held for dandsome. Meanwhile the news was brought that Fingall who was ever allert in visiting his outposts came galloping up with a band of horsemen and glanced at the prisoner who had been just brought in and commenced to laugh heartily to the great discomfort of Young Harrold who now partly guessed the great mistake he and his mates had made. This man is a giant and I am a prisoner in

Fingalls hands. Fingall now asked in a loud voice who was responsuble for the rough handling of his youth, who was surely a messenger of Roger the bold his friend. But no one answered. The situation was now becoming awkward for the young viking, but he was quick of whit and turning to the giant chief he said, if thou wilst but cast off these bonds I am ready to speak to the King of Fingall, for as thou sayest I am the true and only son of my father Roger of the Faroes, and came to ask news of the fleet as I and my crew are following him and would be glad to get news of him as we wish to join him on the High seas. As thou can see this is my Fathers crest I have tatooed deep on my arm and am called by my folks Harold the Webbed and here he opened his fingers and spread wide his Toes. ,Twas Dame Nature made me so but beyond the looks this causes me no discomfort but makes me handy in the rough seas. Harold was now set free, and amid hearty laughter, Fingall declaring to those around him that he had not expected that his coast guards were so dum as to think the Romans were webbed and came to invade his country like fish from out the Surf. After more merriment Harold now asked the Chief if he could signal to his ship was awaiting him round the point of land on which grew the high trees. His wish was granted and once more diving in the sea he broke the news to his ship mates who understood the situation at once and taking in their sea anchor they quickly made sail and came as close to shore as was safe and with a hearty cheer greeted Fingall and his horsemen who were waiting for them. The cheer in Norse was answered in Gallic, Kaith mille Faltas, which means a hundred thousand welcomes. The boys now asked if they could be shown a cove where they might anchor. The great Chief answered them by sending a man on bord at once. They were greatly admired by the Ladies of Fingall as they lined up with strong bows unstrung and held high as a sign of friendship. Whilst their coats of light polished white chain thrown over their brown leather jerkins and their wolf skin caps hung around with light ringlets and braided hair gave them more the appearance of a crew of faries, as the morning sun lit up their beautiful faces and showed up their shapes whilst their ship wore a figure head of a large Greenland Walrus decorated with his natural Ivories. Such a beautiful Vision took the Eyes of all and as the ship made a swift turn towards Fingalls Castle there was a great rush towards the keep to see the grand sight. The pilot now directed them round the large needle shaped islets which were covered by gannets, divers and other sea birds, who were busily feeding their young ones. They then passed between two high pointed rocks also white with sea fowl and quickly clewing up all sail they glided into Fingalls private Keep, the huge copper gates having been opened for them. The inner waters of this large cavern were calm and as the sides of the rockwalls were lit up with torches it surely was a grand sight the galleries above were full of the noble ladies of Old Fingall who waved the lads such a welcome as nere had been heard before, and was re-echoed through Fingalls caverns so that the sea fowl frightened from their cosy homes flew by the vyking ship like various coloured snow. The boys led by Young Harold now climed the stairway made of steps hewn in the solid rock and entered the bigest great hall they had ever seen, and were so surprised they looked it. And as was their home fassion curtsied to the ladies first and then made their bows to Fingalls chiefs. After which they were led to the groening tables set out with such a variety of foods from sea and land whilst the ladies smilingly waited on their guests whilst the Irish harps played fairy tunes and lullabies. And after these young vykings had made a hearty meal the tables were cleared away and most of the ladies had withdrawn full of praise for the stalwart saxon (?) lads whom they all declared were too young to dare the dangers of the Deep, especially as they were unacquainted with the danger of the times. The Ladies of Fingall where just as tender-hearted as their eyes were blue but could not help but admire the galantry of these chainclad boys.

CONVERSATION

"Well, ma'am, it's turned out all for the best, but I got locked in the plot this week for a day or two. 'Twas when I'd landed those truant lads at Fingall's Keep. I'd thought I'd got 'em stuck there. But being a runaway myself it went contrary to my notions of literature to let the hero die too soon. Then what with one thing and another it jumped into my head that I could turn a bad catastrophe into benefice.

"I had a good incentive and it cleared my head. This feller Ormerod turned up and we had a few drinks together and a talk about Lancashire. And in the morning it came on me just as I woke up. Such a wild-looking outfit as those boys'd be sure to cause amusement at court. Then I began to weave out that from amusement came out the news of the lad's father being acquainted with Fingall, and then they were naturally given the agreeable duty of taking an important military message.

"Aye, it came out well. But for a time I was plot-locked. It's when you see a picture that the way out comes. Quite a little find I had when I pictured Fingall's people peering down the staircase to see the captive boys. Fingall being a chief of course'd be exactly *comme il faut*. He was a paramount. Then there were the smaller chiefs and their blue-eyed belles. 'You've never seen an apparition like this before,' they said.

"Aye, you get lots of good bits when you're fast asleep or just waking up. The mind is always apt to paint pictures when on the border land. But you see how I'm holding the story back now to get me equality of solution. I'll get me picturesque sensations, but they must arise like a natural growth. Me pencil's naturally all for rushing into the *mêlée* of the combats I see ahead—scarlet sails and the glitter of the centurions in the rising sun and the twang and clatter of the catapults. But you've got to be frugal of the high lights, George Bussey says.

"Aye, George was a father to you. He'd put you

straight in matters of literary wisdom. A new hand'd always want to put the showy goods first in the window until George held him back. Very good for young fellers, a man like George. Not one iota of vulgarity in Bussey or Dickens. They were genius enough to rely on something clean. It's only second-raters that have to bowl attention to the hinder parts like dirty monkeys.

"Aye, when the messenger calls out 'One Julius Cæsar is about to land' the two chiefs laughed. 'Even now on the French coast the galleys assemble,' he said. They laughed. Fingall and Roger never entertained the reverse side of the word conquest in the mind. The sea was theirs by immemorial right of habit. They wanted no mightier army than the waves and storms of the north. A man's a man for 'a that, but the man that utilises nature'll always be top dog.

"When a nation's all for science and art they're not men at all. When the Romans got engrossed with luxury and education, building villas and so on with all sorts of fancy ornaments, 'twas no incentive to conquest. Even religion's a better incentive to bloodshed than science. Next to a boundary or a bit of disputed coast there's nothing like the cross or the crescent for rousing pugilism. A symbol like that'll beat any war office for martial influence. Is there any flag in the world or other savage totem can lay claim to the bloodshed that's followed the holy tokens of the crescent and the cross? 'Tis religion has kept the fighting instincts of humanity from destruction. Aye, nature surely has a twofold purpose in the instincts she's given to man. When he says his prayers and turns to the east or gets immersed in baptism he doesn't know he's only a catspaw in the schemes of the natural mother of all. Aye, she knows best.

"This so-called science is the natural enemy of war. A man likes to get to natural grips with the cutlass. A cutlass'll keep war to the fore longer than any of these fancy scientists weapons. Poison gas, et cetra, and so forth. No exhilaration at such a distance.

"Excuse me mentioning the scientist in a critical spirit. I know your husband is one. I've met others on the old Ivory once, I think I told you. Nice fellers doing some deep-sea dredging. Prying out the secrets of evolution, so-called. What's evolution but a newfangled name for nature and her hidden doings? No one ever thought of such a name until they dug up a few secrets not meant for human eyes.

"Don't tell me, ma'am, that we were ever meant to pry so deep as to fish up an animal that burst itself there on the deck! Not being used to the pressure of the world's air, but only to a mile or so of salt water, his eyes fell out. Blind eyes, seemingly. But they fell out on the deck. 'Twas a disgraceful spectacle.

"The doctor will know, being a scientist, that the crustacean stands pressure. Fish, to speak to the contrary, have no such resistant power. The water flows through a fish, so there's no pressure for him to withstand, being part of the element he inhabits. One o' the seven wonders of nature is the amount of pressure a whale'll stand. Whalers always have to be ready to pay out a mile of rope when he dives. A proper giant among mammals, to carry a mile of salt water on his back.

"There's a lot of fancy talk about Darwinism, so called. Better be developed from webfeet than from a gorilla in his family tree. Darwinism may be a measure of the truth in the south of Europe that's the home of dagoes, but it'll never be said of the vikings that they rose from anything but the sea. Aye, and with feet webbed for the purpose! Nature can revert as well as go forward for the good of the world. 'Twas she gave the men from the north webby feet and hands for their advance in the element foreordained for their uses.

"Tell me, ma'am, how would a monkey ever have got up to the north pole for us to be descended from? If the monkey as ancestor, why not the manatee? All but human, the manatee. Turn his knees round a bit and give him a pair o' shoes and an umbrella, and he'd make a fair speciman of a man.

"There's strange things in the sea. That's why they ran away from Harold the Webbed when he came out o' the surf. Aye, they thought he was a water lout.

"A water lout? Excuse me, ma'am, I'm forgetting your knowledge of old English is meagre. 'Tis a little animal comes out o' the sea, runs along on legs and has a good look at you and goes off back into the surf without a word. Considered not to be too lucky to see one. Aye, there's a natural superstition dwells by the edges of the sea. The sea surely is the mother o' mystery. 'Tis because it's never still and the barrier surf protects its mysteries.

"Aye, when a lad swims in surf like that around Fingall's coast—and the breakers are spotted with diatoms.

"I used to go swimming there with Hugh X——, my cousin that's Fish Commissioner now. Him that got me on the minesweeper. Depth charge number three I was in the North Sea. Lads in the brine on a summer's day're wanting nothing nearer to life. 'I'm sorry for the Horns,' Dr. R—— used to say at school, 'with such a wild lad.' But I was always top at wrestling and swimming. And I always took the prize for animal painting. But when a lad's wild there's nothing stills him like battling wi' the surf. That'll calm the soul when stools and offices fail to exert a purifying influence.

"Battling out! 'Tis a lad's natural instinct gets full play in the surf. Aye, the so-called temptations of London, Victoria Street, Westminster and so on'll not harm a lad that can beat the breakers as it harms one o' your little office clarks've never been at grips wi' nature. What else have the poor things got for the purposes of exhilaration beyond what they find in the streets?

"Ma'am, if it's fact you're wanting, I've been in Scotland Yard. Number ——, Walworth division, was my number. I know what a London clark has to battle against in the way of attractive temptation. Clarks? 'Twas royalty no less than clarks. Aye, the brotherhood of man is plain to be seen when you watch the streets o' London. There's no difference between the duke and the clark except that the high-up feller can afford his ten pounds for a virgin. A clark must be content with second-hand truck. But the nobility doesn't use anything twice if it can be helped—women or wine glasses, 'tis all the same.

"Aye . . . looking for the demimonde in W—— Street, Pall Mall, watching for royalty. I've seen 'em at it. That G—— Journal thought it'd got a big scoop with that. Financed by an American millionaire the newspaper wanted to share the news. The Americans have always been a moral people. They like to see vice exposed—'tis all that's left of the pleasurable excitement of seeing a witch burnt, or stoning some poor, unvirtuous girl, same as they used to.

"Aye, but that sort doesn't give each other away. Royalty was never betrayed that time. Neither by Scotland Yard nor the demimonde. Let 'em whistle for the news—they'll not pierce the behaviour of a gentleman by bribing all and sundry to betray. There are times, ma'am, when every Englishman becomes a gentleman. *Esprit de corps.* That's what it is, and well understood in London, whether tenement or palace.

"Not but what the Americans're just as anxious to see their own high-up fellers lead the moral life. Although somewhat less topical than royalty, a Governor has his value as a sinner in the newspaper world. I know newspapers, ma'am. 'Tis not the first time I've done writing—come to writing as such. At one time I've done comical columns'd make a dog laugh. Alleghany *Times, Rocky Mountain News,* et cetera, and so forth.

"Nice feller, the editor of the —— was. But he got into some trouble for truth-speaking about Governor X. He'd got rid of his wife. Nice, white-haired woman'd washed gold with him when they were young together. He goes and marries an opera singer, one o' these prima donnas with lemon-coloured hair and a lot of figger. Never did a hand's turn in her life. Naturally Americans won't stand for that sort of thing. In those days they'd got to keep the community pure, even if it was at the point o' the pen.

"But a bit of fearless critique'd often get an editor into trouble. Howbeit he wasn't going to see me suffer for it as well as himself. He gave me a hundred dollars and a pony to cross the ridge with. 'Twas rough going in those days. But in the States it can hail or snow—if you're a man you can travel anywhere.

"Well, ma'am, I mustn't give way to too much talk. But when it's the only place I ever meet a natural curiosity as to the panoramas I've seen in life, 'tis no more than nature that I should express my thoughts.

"I hope you liked the description of the ladies of Fingall's court. I could 'a put more in, but best not insult the susceptibilities of readers. Best not dwell too closely on Fingall's daughters. To tell you the truth, Harold the Webbed was only sixteen, but he was a fine lad with a great thigh on him already. And those white ringlets of his, like silken floss. . . .

"The fine daughters of Fingall were always in demand by Scottish rovers. One of 'em got ravished away to the north once by one o' these Scotch freebooters. So Fingall had to send a punitive expedition to avenge a daughter's honour. They didn't retrieve the poor girl, but they were rewarded in a commercial way none the less. Aye, they brought back a handsome tribute to Fingall's prowess, procured by his premier general. 'Here's the loot,' he says, 'here's the women, and here's ten Scotchmen for ransom.' A constant system of barter by violence kept the tribes healthy in those ancient days. A proper circulation of women and hostages plus the hardware and trinkets attendant upon warfare. According to the dictates of nature. Why, Fingall himself had been to Scotland with Rodger the Bold redressing wrongs. There used to be grand loot in those Scottish castles, bagpipes and claymores. Costly cairngorms. Fine woollen kilts for the women's shoulders——

"Aye, the Irish've always have had a religious antipathy to the Scotch. Same as there is in Lancashire since Prince Charlie came to Preston with a few specimens. He never marched 'em north again. They were sleeping too sound to follow the pipes. In the Scots Field he left 'em. We lads used to play with their heads. We used to run after the ploughman when we saw him riding home in the evening.* 'Did you find a Scotchman's head to-day?' we'd say to him. And sometimes he'd got a skull on his hand for us.

* It must be realised that a ploughman of the old school almost invariably rides home sitting, not astride, but sideways on his horse: a very tired man, his body giving to the slow steps of the tired horse. So there would be ample time for young boys to enquire about Scotchmen's heads.

"Aye. Blowing peas through a Scotchman's head'd always please us for a few days. You know what lads are for a novelty! But no Scotchman came into Lancashire for a donkey's years after the rebellion. None had been seen in the memory of man. And then one day when we were lads a Scotchman came through the villages with the bagpipes looking for pence. You should 'a seen the lads after him, jeering at him and pointing at his bare knees! He didn't come back that way. We never saw another, although I'm told they're common enough now. A Scotchman'll dare any notable disgrace, come to pennies.

"Lads in the country. . . . Always watching for something. 'Tis town days are all of a pattern. In the country some notable event's always ready to arrive. To say nothing of play. There's the natural seasons from pegtops to kites. Marbles and so on in due order. Gunpowder day's a pleasurable interlude to lads. Then there's the masks and so on on Christmas Eve.

"Aye, nature'll always take a hand at amusing boys. When there wasn't a hunt to entertain us there'd be something else bound to happen. I've told you I've seen an old woman stoned for a witch. All the lads after her. Anything against nature like that'll fill a lad with fright plus a natural curiosity. And when you're frightened you're cruel. The instinct to pursue becomes top dog, same as it does in the hunting season. Ladies and gentlemen giving way to a natural barbarity.

" 'Tis when Mister Reynard's hung up a pheasant or two in his larder he has to look out for his brush. When you see a fox this shape over a hedge [describing a crescent shape in the air with his hand] or staring down intent into a ditch you'll know he's looking to see if his food's ripe yet. He's choicey, not greedy. Same as we are with game. We like it well hung.

"The fox has a natural leaning towards pheasant, same as a man. No gentleman'd disturb a fox for a few turkeys. 'Tis looting the pheasant makes 'em eager to be after Lad Reynard.

"One run we had when I was with me uncle Ralph one time. That was a proper chief of his clan, that fox. Enjoyed the game like a man. Got away all right, too; towards Lancaster. I'd think of him sometimes when I'd be waiting for big game. Hoped he was still running. 'Twas enough to make me drop me gun to think of the time when Africa'll have no more than a few jackals left. And those preserved for the pleasure of fellers like Sir A—— B—— or Sir Y—— Z——, and the *haut ton* of that mining camp known as the Golden City. Instead of being paid for at a shilling a tail by a government that's always made a fancy pet of its farmers. Pays 'em for destroying vermin on their own farms! There's some o' these farmers, so called the backbone of Africa, 'll not kill the fleas on their own dogs without crying to Parliament to be paid for the work. Work! 'Tis the native boys do it—come to work as such.

"Well, ma'am, I'm glad my literary notions're pleasing you. History plus the fair sex has always been a winner.

"Aye, the ladies were greatly taken with that webbed lad. He surely provided a novelty in the great keep. 'Don't harm him,' they said to their father, 'the bonny lad in ringlets!' And the sand still on the webs between his toes. An apparition in white ringlets! A human sea-bird! And landing there to seize tribute from a giant like Chief Fingall. Seven foot four he was. A grand figure of a man. When he heard his daughters laugh, out popped their father, the chief, from an audience he'd been having with his officers, to see what they'd been laughing about. A veritable comedy.

"Aye, they were greatly tickled at the sight of him. The old Walrus tusking its way into the keep and young Harold standing at the prow—a proper vision of nobility, though only a lad in a prank.

"If you like, ma'am, you can embellish the scene a little further if you happen to be thinking of cinemas. I've held back, but if it's for a cinema you'll need no restraint. *Homo stultus* watching a cinema kaleidoscope has to be treated like a child—knowing nothing, he's got to have the pictures painted bright. Well, I'll leave it to you, ma'am, to empty the paintbox on it."

CHAPTER IV.

AFTER the hearty meal the boys had made and the Royal ladies had returned the Saxon [Norse?] lads naturally born without reservation of rank in the island homes were curious and with childlike simplicity examined the shields battle axes and armour which adorned the Great Hall in Fingalls keep and many of them then went forth and climed the heights wending their way along the passages from the Hall and Cavern. Below them in view in the valley they could see the old King and his chiefs watching the manoevers of his foot and Cavallry but he had no Bowmen, and at this they wondered, many of them remarking how long that man and so on would stay on horseback if I had the bow on him and they even laughed at the mannerisms of the footmen with their shields and long swords whilst O'Gaunt the Son of the shipbuilder laughingly remarked, How long would it take such men as these to take our island from us. This was an object lesson to these lads, which lasted them long into the future. After all has been sayd and done the worth of the strong bow revolutionised the world as far as british Speakers are concerned and for proof of this we can cite such famous battales as Poitiers, Cressy and the famous field of Agincourt where every dead man, Knight or commoner wore a well planted Saxon arrow. Still the boys wondered at the marvelous endurance of these men, as they attacked hill after hill and then with quickness in long lines they swung into step to the quick and shrill tune of the pibrooks (Irish bagpipes). This was a small levy of Fingalls men being trained for duty in the newly acquired country North-west-Scotia and were preparing when found fit by Fingall for duty against Julius Seasar or anybody Else. And they were surely fit when passed by this great fighting chief who was in his day the pride of Scotland and Ireland as their folk lore relates, and was never defeated. After clearing from the field and well fed, these troops were taken to Bathing parade and then came their whiskey tots quite big ones and a rest up. They were now marched for two or three hours being heavily knapsacked, and then the rest of the day was theirs. But Woe betide the Evil-doer or disobedient, in those days. He was tried by his own comrades and if found guilty was subjected to punishment ad lib by his own regiment who not unoften laid him out as fitting punishment and this tryal by his Peers was found the best sauce at all times, and was considered just and fair by all, even by the evil doers themselves, and was satisfactory to all. And now the lads returned to the great Hall having learned the lesson of how Fingall became great. They now discussed their going away, as they felt sure of loot further south, and whilst they were arranging for quick going they were stayed by the enterance of the King and his fighting chiefs, and along with them came a Sage or wise man who could speak and write in many tongues, and had just received a message that Saesar and his army were now ready for the invasion of Brittain and were only awaiting the first fine day so they could make their landing somewhere upon the coast. Then Fingall bade all but those needed round him to retire and calling the lads around him he told them of the new pact he had made and unfolding a large paparus sheet, he showed them the fist seal of their fathers at this the lads lad like were forced to smile as they could well make out the size of each ones fist and could even say their names, this made the great chief laugh and also his generals at the quick sight and wit of these Saxon lads. Then in a box of fine sand he explained by drawing a map of South Brittain, about where Ceasar and his great army would cross over, and also about where the lads could expect to find their fathers fleet of 40 sail, who were waiting to loot Ceasars Convoys. This was exciting news to the boys who said they had understood and then Spoke O'Gaunt the navigator who had sailed often with his father and he praised the chart drawn by the Sage. And to prove this he took a little sand and made a small mound called Manxland or the Isle of man and then a small one further south towards Harlech Castle called Innis Castle (Bardsey Island). Then inland from Abermean (Mandac) he made a taller mound, Ceddar Idderis and continued heaping smaller and biger piles of sand at last showed the Chalk Cliffs opposite the Frankish coast, opposite but a little to the northard of where the sage marked the Roman camp. The King and chiefs as well as the sage here marvelled at the knowledge of this lad, who they declared to be born with full knowledge of his whereabouts at sea. And now being anxious to go they begged the King, as they had well understood his advise, which was to return if any move were made by the Romans in the Irish sea or toward the Coast of Cambria (now Whales) and to watch keenly the Coast of the Manx Islands for Foreign shipping, to let them depart. But the Old Chief replied I have runners on the coast of Erin and have been expecting horse dispatch since morning so let me ask you as you are fleet at sea, to wait and I will tell you what this last news conveys so that I can foil any move towards the coast of Erin or Scotia and will be better able to advise Sir Rodger of the roman moves which will greatly help us in the common cause. And calling on his Muller to bring in a loving bowl, bade these young Saxons Kindly wait. To which they agreed saying Your one of our Allies we are under your beck and call, we have our fathers seal to witness we are entirely guided by you King Fingall. Now in came the great copper mull carried by the stalwart men and Fingall handed out the horn of spiced hot ale to all, drinking last himself. The meeting was over and on the toll of going out in came Fingalls queen with her daughters and attendants with such music as might be pleasing in these anxious times. And the King bade the Saxons not to be shy, as he had noticed they were backish, which was only natural in boys brought up in keep of the Island Kings. And after a little coaxing mixed with the tune of the great harps the Irish noble Ladies with their kind words and love glints in their eyes had soon won the affections and overcome the reticence of these children of the sea, as a kind word from a lady makes all lads soften and is welcome at all times by young and old. At the good queens request for a song from the lads they all arose and asked what kind of song she would like, as they could Warble the Wind songs and Echoes and had quite a long list but could only sing to their own wild music which they generally accompanied by the Saxon harp and fiddle. At this the good lady was really pleased and ordered her harpers to hand over their instruments to the boys, who after tuning up both fiddle and harp to suit themselves chorussed a lullaby something after the stile of the modern Rock a by baby with variations. This over the Mussicians of Old Fingall were quite taken up by the sweet voices of the singers who were loudly enchored. The North winds blow and several other songs being sung the lads now sung the Echo songs which were so wild and pretty that All present were quite taken aback. They had never expected anything like this to come from the young sailors, who keenly appreciated the surprise they had caused. Next the young Harold called on a youngster but turned fifteen, who like his father was a dancer and mimmacker and was well known throughout the Faroes for his talent. The harp and fiddle now produced a jig tune to which he kept time with nimble feet and now commenced a sword dance which greatly took his audience and wound up with jigs and pedestal dancing always keeping exact time with the music seemingly without effort it was all second nature to him. On finishing this roll as dancer he was loudly chheered and enchored, whilst he immitated the sea gulls the honk honk of the wild geese and then after whistling the skylark from his nest to a great height in the air and then mimmicked the drooping songster back to his nest the great Hall was filled with surprise and sounds of Applaus. The good queen kindly drew the youngster towards her and patting him on the head and stroking the lads curly locks she bade him take a rest. He was the greatest surprise they ever had. After resting he made a bow to the ladies and finished his turn by immitating Irish bagpipes with his mouth and so natural and like were the sounds he made as he marched to and fro with the martial swing of a piper that when he broke off and resumed his seat the Hall was filled with shouting and laughter. He was the hero of the hour and well he deserved his praise. The harpers now took their seats and sword dances accompanied by the pipes were greatly enjoyed. Many of the ladies were experts at their native hornpipes and the boys were thoroughly enjoying the evening when a messenger arrived bringing a paparus missive carrying news of the movements of the Romans. Fingall and his Sage now arose and learned what a large number of Roman galleys had joined Seasar who was making all preparations to embarke with his large army. Calling Harrold and his first mate and Navigator aside, he gave them the news and also his last message for Sir Roger and his fleet and telling them to sail if possible and skirt the Manx Island and then hug the Cambrian coast and report to Sir Roger what they might see of interest to the commonwheal, this they promised to do and bidding good buy after drinking a loving cup with Fingall who had well provisioned their ship, they prepared to set sail at once.

CONVERSATION

"You've read it, ma'am? Sitting here with a garden to look at instead of the street and old Sol embracing me I can keep no count of time. You read very quickly or else I've been dreaming.

"Well, I've got a few fancy novelties there for you. And more to come. Something fresh, that's what readers want. Varied food for the brain as well as the stomach. You can't live a week even on pheasants. I've tried it—between two rivers. Food gave out and we'd nothing but pheasants. Even a king's vittles'd get nauseating if there was a prospect of nothing else.

"I thought you'd appreciate the little bit about that lad making maps in the sand. That's a bit of knowledge that's natural, like folk lore. I hate to go into a library and read things I'd have thought of for myself. It makes me sick to add to my knowledge with other fellers' books. Aye, it's better to make books than to read 'em. It revives the intellect. Provides recreation and so on to battle out for an idea. Same with riches. It's better to make fresh money than to disturb your sleep trying to save old gains. Whether yours or your grandfather's. Better for the intellect to battle out. Seize something for yourself and you're a better man for it.

"Aye, me best books of so-called reference is the knowledge that came natural to me through experience. When a thing's true it rings good. I don't hold with reading if it can be helped. Too softening. A bit of Shakespeare and Lingard's all I ever need.

> Naught shall make us rue
> If England to itself do rest but true.

Aye, when you meet a truism like that! Shakespeare got it from the priests, but it's been well known in Lancashire since the viking occupation. The monks were likely thinking of the older church, but in Lancashire before the church was a *fait accompli* the bow was defending England. There was always the bow to fall back upon. Be true to the bow and you'll be true to England.

"Two hundred to the minute from the yards. A crew of forty we'd have and shooting their five arrows to the minute. Experts could shoot ten to the minute. As good and swift as a six-shooter.

"The boys laughed when they saw Fingall's clumsy notions *re* fighting. Big swords, suitable for giants such as Fingall's levies were, but lacking that natural genius of the bow and arrow. We've got to copy nature to get the most practical ideas. A feathered weapon—what's it studied from but the wild birds of the north?

" 'Twas a pretty art they had, the arrowsmiths of Lancashire. When I was a lad there still were Arrowsmiths, family of that name, plying their trade as such. 'Twas a choicey bit of craftmanship. Placing the feathers the hundredth part of an inch wrong would make all the difference. Goose quill it had to be. Ma'am, I can see that those grey goose feathers gave us a flight that didn't stop in centuries. Doesn't every Lancashire man look up when he hears the geese passing over, even if 'tis only one or two? 'Tis a sound stirs his blood, same as the old sea-horn used to. Aye!

"From those very fellers who were shooting arrows from the yards came railways and the spinning-jenny. Nature gave them the instinct to use their wits when living got poor. Lancashire'll always be able to move when the other races approach stagnation. Even if it's back to the bow for defence, Lancashire moves. And when all else fails we'll take to the sea for safety. Grow our webby feet again. An enemy can knock your big ships out of action but he'll never capture the arrow. In the ultimate 'tis the arrow will be England's getaway. She can always make a fresh start from the goose feather plus the sea.

"Aye, the old fist and spear've always seized a living from the sea. There was me greatuncle Dick that was the last of the buccaneers and had a house in M—— Road, Hyde Park. Property in Savannah. Massive silver and so on and so forth in his London house. But Savannah always called him to a natural life.

"And there was me greatuncle Horn. Stone blind. Always sitting in the little chair by the fire. But he pulled big power over the family. He got to over ninety, but age couldn't wipe out his knowledge of the shipping trade. All the family meetings were held in the parlour where greatuncle Horn sat. After a meet in the neighbourhood all me uncles and men cousins would finish up the hunting with a conclave for business purposes in the drawing-room. Clear out the ladies and shut the door.

"Aye, old man Horn pulled big power until he died. Blind as he was, he'd not be content to act the greybeard in his little chair. He knew things young 'uns'd fail at. 'Is she very thin on the waterline?' he'd say. Always listening. 'Too high in the prow . . . we must extend the keel for spring . . .' he'd say to himself. Then he'd have to jump up and sweep himself a place with his cane. Draw the lines of a new vessel on the carpet with his stick, as if he could see her there. Aye, he knew the anatomy of ships blind better than his grandsons and nephews. 'And here'll be her vulnerable spot,' he'd say. Could draw a chart with his blind eyes better than any of 'em. They respected his knowledge, ancient as he was and the light gone from his eyes.

"Aye, the firm'd always done a lot of business supplying ships to South America or other warlike neighbourhood. Any country that's taken to revolution is a hidden blessing to a shipbuilding family. There's a silver lining to every little revolution, so-called. Meaning a period of dago antics with firearms. Leave the straw hat in the office and proceed to mimic battle armed with gold lace et cetera and so forth. Epaulettes.

Comical fellers, come to fighting. They'd run from a cutlass.

"What's that, ma'am? Well, of course, business is business. They say all's fair in love and war. And who's to know how a revolution'll end? You might get nothing from the losing side. But if you sell the knowledge of the vulnerable spot to a customer's enemy, then you're fortified against loss. One o' the old privileges of the trade. The feller that builds the ships is bound to be top dog.

"Aye, me Greatuncle Horn. Over ninety, and needn't 'a died then if he hadn't asked to ride on the hay load. Always had a longing for the smell o' the hay. When the haymaking was on he'd sit there against a haycock in the sun, feeling it with his fingers and filling his nostrils with the aromas in the breeze. But one day when they were leading,* and they'd got to the last cock, he begged to be put atop o' the hay wagon. Perhaps he had a natural suspicion that the next haymaking would proceed without him. So they lifted him up and Greatuncle Horn sank into the nice nest they'd made top o' the load. They heard him laugh to himself. . . .

" 'Twas the last they heard of old man Horn's voice. Going over a bad bit o' the field, the wagon rocked and the old man fell off. Broke his back. When you're blind the sense of balance suffers.

"Aye, he never spoke again. He'd had his say.

* Gathering in the dried hay: the last process in the hayfield, much appreciated by boys.

Pulled big power all his life and had a bit of natural fun to finish with. There's always something meagre about dying in a bed.

"Aye, there's fellers here harbour a feeling of animosity against dying in the disarray of a bed. 'Tis a gentleman's instinct. When they can seize no more for themselves and they daren't sell a bottle * or haven't the money to buy one, they'll brush 'emselves neat every night and manage to get along to those seats in the square or opposite the market down there. They get afraid to leave the seat for fear they should lose their dignity by dying in the gutter. A feller likes to be found in good order when the ultimate has beckoned him. 'Tis a gentleman's instinct not to create a furore in streets.

"They've found one or two like that, if all records were known. Death from natural causes and hustle 'em away. Oh, aye, it's natural enough to die when you can seize no more food. There's a shocking modicum of truth in the diagnosis.

"But they couldn't stop the truth escaping about that poor feller found in the goods yard last week. A soldier and found dead of starvation. 'Tis pride killed him, they'll tell you. 'Isn't there relief societies he could 'a gone to?' But it's not to everybody's taste to give way to relief. I've used relief myself and been thankful for the offer. Same as I'd use a dead cricket for a wound and the services of a witch doctor when I

* To a native. A punishable offence in South Africa.

couldn't call up Harley Street. But there's some fellers can't fall back on philosophy. What all these committees are too ignorant to grasp is that those medals and testimonials he had in his pocket are just what killed him. Suicide by pride is what I'd call it. He had a letter from Winston Churchill in his pocket, but that wouldn't go far here. 'Tis the gold standard here.

"Aye. There he lay, a yard from the rails, and well within sound of the masons putting up the monument. That monument's some years behind the times, come to soldiers lying in France. Or Mesopotamia, where my lad is. But it'll serve to commemorate that feller with medals in his pocket.

"A letter from Winston Churchill. . . .

"Well, ma'am, I mustn't keep you with gossip. One is apt to overdo conversation when you get only one a week. I'll be getting along with the narrative easy now. A feller always writes better when he knows some one's going to read his ideas. Oblivion's what silences the pen.

"I shall be weaving you in some popular bits about omens and so on. You get lots of literary notions when you're half asleep or just waking up. It occupies the mind, too, which is an advantage when you're living with the *summa cacumni* [?] of rascality. Aye, it purifies the air. Helps a feller to breathe.

"A big paramount chief like Fingall, savage as he might now be considered, was exactly *comme il faut*. Etiquette was thought very highly of in those wild courts of the earlies. The household of a powerful chief was never complete without the wiseman to read omens and so on. All the chiefs of Britain had their sages. Beauclarks they called 'em in high society, but sage or wiseman is an old English word, sounds better in literature. Bussey always crossed out the lengthy words. He was always for purifying the language.

"Aye, all the paramounts had their wisemen. Fellers that wanted to travel and improve the mind. They knew they'd not be hurt. Every chief must have wisdom beside him, even if he scorned it. Take any hereditary chieftain, like Lord Derby, or Howard o' Glossop. If all secrets were known you'd find scorn of the learned clarks still there. 'My hand and seal' is degree enough for a gentleman. Always was. A gentleman from immemorial times has had to chance his arm to earn the title. But come to clarks or beauclarks, lawyers or clergymen, they never chance anything, whether in historical times or the present. Aye, the churches teach us the Lord will provide but neither clark nor clergy could 'a moved across the world except behind the shield of the fighting men.

"Excuse me, ma'am, keeping you in conversation at the gate. But if it's thoughts you're wanting, I can easy make you a thinking novel. Something above the realms of cinema.

"But it'd not sell too easy. They want sensations in America since prohibition became the rage. Deny nature one way and she'll get what she wants in another.

The use of incentives has always provided a sensible outlet for the imagination.

"We must think of the Americans, ma'am. It's no use making notes on prohibition if you've got no novelists amongst your facts. Present a fact as if it were a novelty, George Bussey used to say, and the reader comes nibbling like a trout after a clever-made fly. So we'll pop in George Washington for a lure. *His father ran a still.* That'll provide novelty plus sensation. Whether it was illicit or not we could hardly insult America by investigating. 'Twould be going too far.

"Aye, prohibition. . . .

"Every island on the Trinity has its still. Look at Jonathan Rider. Any one came nosing around he was politically strong enough to see 'em disappear.

"Strange feller, Jonathan Rider. Although a millionaire he's never been satisfied. Must always have something further. Something beyond the dreams of avarice, as the saying is. He carried a gun. Money without a gun at the back of it'd never satisfy Jonathan Rider. I knew him well. Lived for some time at his place near X——, Georgia. With so many private interests hidden in the plantations and on the islands, he needed a few reliable friends to act as sentries. Overseer and so on.

"Aye, Jonathan Rider. . . .

"The way I met him was sure one of the curious novelties engineered by fate. 'Tis the pagans called it fate. But after becoming acquainted, as I did, with

Jonathan Rider the goddess surely wore the sweet smile of the protecting saints.

" 'Twas all dependent on a plate of fish bestowed in a moment of charity. . . .

"Excuse me, ma'am, I see that you're wanted in the house. Well—here's to *au revoir.*"

CHAPTER V

As the lads rose and made their farewell bow to the Royal assembly they were loudly cheered whilst Fingalls queen planted a kiss on the forehead of the youngest one, who then amidst the din of cheers loudly imitated the song of the black throstle and then broke off into the warbles of the thrush, turning as he retired he threw the sounds at Fingall and his Lady, and as he descended the stone stairway, followed by the laughing crowd he loudly gave the Kaw Kaw of the vexed raven and to the great amusement of the multitude ran up the rigging and catching the crosstrees with his bent knees he imitated the flight and cry of the sea mew. A garland of pinks and shamrocks was now put around the old walrus Figurehead. The long sweeps were put out and a few strokes of these long oars took the ship out into the silvery moonlight forming a great contrast to the reflections of the great torchlights golden Hues and seemed like the passing of a fairy ship from gold to silver light. And amidst the thunders of oplause for the boys who were going to meet Ceasar the sails were set taught and merrily dancing away to the south away sped the vyking ship carrying good wishes and the hearts of Fingall and his ladies with her. The young sailors were in high glee, and as they sped south those on watch turned too, whilst the rest were soon sleeping soundly dreaming of what they had seen. The watch kept good look out but all was peaceful and the morning found them well away to the southerd. They now tacked out from the coast of Erin and accompanied by the sea birds headed for Mona (Isle of Man) and by sundown were sailing merrily down the east coast of the Island, which as the evening came on with bright moonlight gave them a good chance of seeing what sails there were on the coast of Mona, whilst the island inhabitants lay gently slumbering. The boys as is a sailors habit, spent the night in sleeping whilst those not ready to turn in whiled away the time yarn spinning. The sea birds as usual were the first indicators of sunrise, as they flew seaward in search of food, and as each coast has its peculiar colours for the same birds, for instance the Nun gull with a black cap on his head and black tips on his wings may be seen today on the shores of the Isle of Man and the Lancashire coast and likewise the coast of North Wales, and is a sure indicator to sailors of their whereabouts. And this no matter on which part of the ocean you may be, you will find the birds a help in navigation providing you are a child of nature and follow natures Edicts, you will see even by the different flight of sea birds how often is heralded to the sailor the brewing of a storm as the old grey gull becomes quicker of wing and more anxious in his search for food, as with a full feed he is better able to ride out the storm, so that when a ship is battened down and half reefed the gull in his western ocean passage sleeps on the seas breast head under wing, surrounded by a ball of feathers lighter than the lightest cork, whilst the Ocean Eagle sleeps on his yearly passage from Morocco to the Indies but vol planing, uses not his wings in effort of flight, that would mean exhaustion, and long long years ago proved the routundity of our world by joining together in his flight the Eastern and Western emispheres. And all it wanted was a thinking man who understood the make up of the feathered race, to have proved to the Sages of the times their error in not remarking [the lesson of the] setting suns. And as I have often thought of doctrines still ixisting Nature will always lead one right if we will but be observant and listen to true wisdom. Thus unknowingly with his bow and arrow which was natures best weapon of the times, together with his swift sea craft the sailor revolutionised the world. Now the lads kept a sharp look out as the island of Mona was a great trading place and being nearly centerally situated, was within easy access to the Coasts of both Erin and Britain. As the sun rose above the Cambrian mountains showing up snow on the peak of Cadiridis whose heads were lit up by the suns rays the lad sitting aloft near the ships cross trees gave the wellcome cry Sail Ohoi. The navigator now quickly climed the rigging and described the sail as a market boat Bound to the Cambrian coast and also said, we are quickly gaining on her and will be ready to overall her before the sun is three hands high (i.e. above the horison). And now all got busy restrung their bows, and got ready for boarding, and as they bowled swiftly along and the ships came gradually nearer they could see the strange ship was heavily laden and carried many passingers amongst whom were several women. And now they gradually closed on the flying vessel and O'Gaunt shouted laughing in disgust that it was simply a village boat with a load of cattle and pigs, sheep and old men, and some of the wenches carried babies tied to their backs in shawls. The arrows and weapons were quickly laid a side, and as they drew close to the ship a javelin was thrown by an old whiskered longhaired man and pinned the wallrus figurehead below the eye, whilst some of the men folk who were armed with shields of bullocks hide and spears shouted laughingly good shot. And one of their number shouted in Cambric good morrow friends, and all the Norse lads answered the greeting. And sailing together a parley took place between the pilot and the Welsh captain, who enquired whence they came and where they were bound and he was well pleased with their answer. The Welsh skipper said he plainly saw they were of the Vyking breed but as he had met such before he knew he was safe from paying toll being a Cambrian from the River Mandac. Here one of the passingers who was somewhat of a humerous wag broke in, saying he was sorry they were honest Norsemen and if they wanted to take any toll from him, he wished them to take his wife, who had ruined him buying gugaws (Fancy womens goods) in Mona and all he got for his copper (he was a miner) she wore on her back. At this all on board laughed heartily and the lads joined the merriment. The good Welsh skipper now asked the sailor lads if they would join them in a drink of strong Mead, which he said was Monas Best, and the lads willingly accepted the offer of a Jar full, which was handed in a net swung to a ships pale hook, were soon smacking their lips at the good tasting liquor which was effervescent and was far better than anything they had drunk before. And returning the compliment they gave the good hearted Welshman two flaggons of Fingalls whiskey. Which they all declared was the best of its kind, the women and girls all drinking from one large horn pulled wry faces but enjoyed it. These ladies young and old were as pretty a lot as could be seen and looked well in their home spun wool shawls and sandals, and were lavishly tattooed on breasts and shoulders whilst their long hair neatly combed and interlaced by small woven ribands of various colours floated out with the sea breeze and made a pleasant contrast to the rather fierce tanned faces of their fathers and menfolks. But nothing could be heard of any strange vessels only that four [40?] ships had been seen sailing south along the shores of Mona about ten days before and the fishermen who saw them in the night said they were vykings from the north. They knew nothing of Julius Seasar and laughed merrily when they heard he was coming to take the whole of the world, and the old great grandfather who was in his cups and had thrown the Gavelin, cried in a loud voice, let this foreigner come to Mandac we will surely give him a good welcome, but all declared they had heard nothing about Romans who they did not know but if they wanted Britain in the South they could have that but no man could live further North and so the druids told them and that had proven true. Who set his foot on land as far as Cadors Eye could see around its base was Doomd. And as they had brought mistletoe on parting from their home and had consulted the druids of the Mandac as to their voyage these priests had given them a large bunch of mistletoe which was now hanging to the mast and had brought them such luck that they had drank Erins best and Monas mead. After much merriment as they sailed together the lads gave them one more flaggon of Fingalls And receiving in return two jars of honey mead of Monas make They excused themselves as they were in haste, but the old great grand father would have none of it they must he said sail together four more fingers of the sun as he wished to learn more of the Sismacks [Welsh for Saxons]. And the ladies and all the men called for a song from the Vyking lads. And what could they do but do it. The young lad the mimmic, now standing alongside threw to them the song of the thrush as he whistled each note perfectly fell off suddenly to breaking a snail shell on a stone in the brook and then ended by giving them several long beautiful bird notes, which sounded so clear one would think the sound came from a brook glade. Here the ladies cheered, that was far beyond them, but in turn they gave a choral song in which all joined, and were accompanied by the sweet sounding Welsh Harp. The sounds came in waves as the waves rode the ships and surely was such music as never is heard in our modern times. And when all were more or less in their cups they called for another song from the lads. The youngest lad now gave them the skylark and when he whistled the bird out of sight with his twisted tongue and holding his wolf skin cap in his hand and pointing to the sky, with clear faraway notes and then followed her to the nest in one swift drop he put his hands down and turning to the Cambrian boat he gave them the caw caw of the vexed raven and making a bow to all was loudly cheered by the Cambrians and the Old Man who had thrown the Javelin sent a Druids blessing on such lads as these. And now the call song was sung to the strings of the Cambrian harp and sounded in melody like the Gwineth Gwin of more modern tunes. And for once (if such could be) hearing the heavenly music on the sea Old Father Neptune did pop up his head and wished a blessing on each singers head. And now the boys though they were loth to go again begged leave, and as they said they were roving the seas without homes but promised to come again even to their homes in Wales to this the brave Cambrians consented althow with regretts So dropping sail which had been half reefed the norse ship turned due south amidst the great cheers and cryes of Wellcome Sysmacks to Cambria. And the boys motioning and pointing to the sea threw in two more flaggons of Fingalls best. And the Cambrian captain changed his course and thanketh them by the up and down signalling of the top sail a seamans sign of old time for a big Good buy and a thank you.

CONVERSATION

"I've slipped in a bit of nature for a refresher this time, ma'am. A bit of nature in a narrative'll always attract a gentleman. In a town like this that can be writ *stultus* in the educated world, there's no fancy for birds and so on unless caged to their doom. But go along the English coast or in the glades and dells o' Lancashire and you'll find that it's a gentleman's habit to observe the workings of nature as indicated by the birds and other creatures.

"I sometimes fancy I might 'a been a bit of a naturalist myself if I'd given way to watching, same as Waterton did. Charles Waterton, one o' the older church. I should 'a kept up my rivers. 'Tis better to spy on the pretty habits of nature than to have to trap a fellow human, which I had to do as a Scotland Yarder. I enjoyed the chase. 'Twas an agreeable pastime for a youngish man. But come to capture—ma'am, it's not for a gentleman to set a woman crying. They always cry when their man's caught. They look at you. . . .

"Aye, if I'd stayed up my rivers on the Ivory I might 'a made a name for myself as Waterton did. South America was where he observed nature. Given a few more years than the so-called allotted span I'd like to do a bit myself in South America some day. I often think there'll be some time wasted in the heavenly hereafter might well be spent in places you've had no time to get acquainted with in the span of life.

"Aye, Waterton. He sent all his beautiful birds he collected to England addressed to the British Museum,

Bloomsbury. But when he found that England expected him to pay duty on his gift to the nation he fell back on his dignity and withdrew the offer. 'Twas a sharp lesson to the authorities not to be so free with red tape. 'Tis these office fellers'll never understand a gentleman and a roamer. Does the sight of a heavenly bird, bright as the rainbow, and never been seen in London, release their imagination? Never did and never will. They're a race apart, office fellers. Clapping the word duty in front of men've seen the world unspoilt. Risked his life for knowledge and beauty and the rudiments of science—that was his notion of duty. And comes home to have a bit of red tape dangled in front of his nose before he can have the privilege of bestowing a notable gift to the nation.

"He gave his birds to the school where my brother Richard was. Him that's a priest. Ushaw, Durham. One of the notable schools where the hereditary chiefs of England send their sons.

"I thought you'd appreciate that bit about the ocean eagle. No need for inquisitions and all that religious toggery to punish Columbus for his belief in an unknown side of the map. The rotundity of the world the birds have always tried to show us. God meant us to learn from nature. Turn your eyes away from nature and you're punished. Transgress the laws of nature and take to orthodoxy and she'll make you suffer for it.

"Aye, the birds proved the roundness of the world. If we hadn't been too busy with orthodoxy we should 'a noticed it for ourselves, same as Columbus did. Even the old grey gull of Lancashire knew about America before Columbus did. Didn't he obey his ideas and go over every year to America and back?

"Aye, he wants to ramble. He's like a Liverpool-born lad—no sooner does he see a sailing-vessel than he wants to leave his mother. Off every year to see the New World while Julius Cæsar was nosing round the river mouths of Britain, well pleased with his discovery of England. But he must come back to lay his eggs on Gillmoss. 'Tis the rambler cherishes the one spot called home. Bird or human, if you never leave the nesting-place the imagination is apt to suffer.

"Aye, the grey gull blazed the trail for Lancashire men for the New World. When that ship's load o' stiffs left Liverpool to fight for the honour of the Lone Star State they were only obeying the dictates of instinct, same as he does. England'd had its chance. Didn't Bill Austin offer Texas to England? In the streets of Liverpool for good money down he'd 'a sold her. But England wasn't taking any more responsibility. She wouldn't put her hand down.

"Aye, they lost a golden opportunity of finding a safe base on American ground. Fine country! . . .

"There was a lot of to-do at Frea about it. Always some excitement there, come to new idea of territory. After the American war between North and South Lancastrians were naturally keeping an open eye for privileges'd make up for the loss of the slave trade. The eighteen-sixty hit the whole world of seafaring men. Might as well take his barrow from a coster as expect shipping families to thrive without the trade. The war made an end of everything. No more slavery on the West Coast. No more piracy. Why, even in the fifties a man could sign on to certain vessels with the full knowledge that he'd share and share alike with the captain. Same as when we were vikings together.

"Aye, that North and South affair surely took away some o' the legitimate rights of the Horns, to say nothing of Queen Victoria. Rights o' piracy, rights o' foreshore, and a fifth to the Queen. He'd always clung to the rights of his ancestors, had me greatuncle Horn, although the contract with the Queen had naturally fallen into abeyance, she being of the newer church, but born lacking in the freebooting instincts of Elizabeth.

"My greatuncle Horn was always fond o' me. Aye, he always encouraged my notions about leaving school and going to sea. He'd promised me a ship when I was old enough. Helped a good many young fellers to get a start in life. Advanced 'em a ship. Say a vessel cost four thousand pounds, he'd let 'em pay it out in pirated booty brought to him. But it wasn't so easy to pay off your debts of honour in those days of respectability—Albert the Good and so on. Very often a poor privateer'd find it difficult to meet with a piratable ship and he'd be obliged to turn towards the West Coast and waylay a slaver. Leave the slaves on the coast—an act of humanitarianism if regarded rightly—and take the vessel to greatuncle Horn.

"It was the failure of the slave trade filled Liverpool with unemployed. A tough lot and only too glad to get a little honest occupation conquering the Lone Star for the benefit of a couple of Liverpool desperadoes—Jack Dallas and Bill Austin.

"Come to desperadoes, it takes nothing more than a bit of success to turn 'em into emperors. Bill Austin had a somewhat less aristocratic field than Buonaparte, but his notions were the same, taken all in all. Look at Rhodes! What with Victoria and one thing and another he had to be content with riches. Diamonds and so on. And get his ambitions pacified making a so-called chartered company instead of obeying his nature with a bit o' cutlass work.

"That feller'd 'a been fine at the Battle of Hastings.

"Aye, Victoria . . . Albert'd have liked to keep her opening bazaars and doing her water-colours, but she wasn't without a natural gift of reach out, come to territory. Any more than Bill Austin was. Or Elizabeth. Always had an eye on Lancashire. It worried her to death to think she couldn't be Queen of Lancashire. It's nothing but a dukedom for the monarchs of England. And they've got to be content with that. The paramount chief himself, Lord Derby, had no need to doff his hat to her unless he wished to observe the privileges of any gentleman in the company of ladies.

"Aye, once rouse Lancashire and you'll never get them put down. Any more than you could stop the head waters of one o' my rivers.

"Fancy her wanting the rights o' Lancashire! Why, Disraeli had to tell her she'd lose her head if she destroyed the Duchy of Lancashire. 'I'm the Queen of England!' she says to him. 'Very true, my girl,' he said to her, 'but not of Lancashire.' She cried and stamped her foot.

"Aye, he had to soothe her down a bit. That's why he made her Empress of India. A bombastic title when you look at the fact that she'd never set foot there any more than I have. But there's something in the contemplation of the unknown that's good for subject races. Look at this country! Wild fellers like Lobengula and other paramounts'll find it easy to pay homage to an unseen female. Great White Queen and so on. When every savage goes in fear of the unseen 'tis easy to keep 'em quiet with an idea like that. You've got to mix a modicum of voodoo with your handling of natives or they'll not understand you. Hang up an almanac of Victoria in her ribbons and jewelry, keep your word to a savage, and never show fear. Quite easy, but there's some races'll never learn the trick.

"The fuss these Portuguese make . . . comical little fellers to look at. I've often had a good laugh to meself. . . .

"Taken all in all, there's only one of the lot ever had big notions, and that was Duke Henry of Portugal. But look who his mother was. John o' Gaunt's daughter! 'Twas the Lancashire streak pushed Henry into activities with ships. Couldn't keep his hands off a sailor. He sure had the smell of the ships in his nostrils. And all through the mother. Hadn't she heard viking talk, same as I did, when she was little? Aye, and some spot like Gillmoss always harping in her mind when she went to live amongst foreigners, poor lass. You can see where he caught his notions.

"The mother—all good comes from the mother. That's what dog breeders say. All the family archives're stored in the female brain. These so-called genealogists don't show that she's the paramount, but nature's not always obtruding her best notions. 'Twould never do. But when a woman turns amazon, like some of those on the old coast, it's neither more nor less than obeying the secret dictates of nature, that stores common sense with the female.

"Aye, nature knows she's more faithful than the male to her responsibilities, so-called. 'Tis this cherishing the unborn teaches the woman to cover up her clever notions. When she begins to talk about 'em she'll lose caste. Nature's storehouse must keep the door locked if there isn't to be trouble in the ultimate.

"Why, there'd not be too many nosegays at Kirkham Glade in cowslip time if nature disclosed the clever secrets of the soil and the running sap. Beauty can't grow its roots in the open any more than I'd have a good notion for a bit of poetry in a saloon or on the streets here. It'd come easier in the Walworth division than in the Golden City, sunshiny though it is.

"Aye, there's a soft heart under London. London was never built on gold. . . .

"That's why poetry and all literary notions grow easy there. Look at Chaucer. Dan Chaucer he was called. A busy feller, like Shakespeare. That's why he knew humanity exactly. It's the busy fellers get the ideas. An idle man has too much time on his hands to get an idea. Sitting in an armchair never brought you nearer to good literary notions. Dickens was busy too. Caught his best notions in Poverty Square. Always wanted something that never came within the ken of his compeers. Did very poorly at journalism until he began advertising for a blacking firm. Billposting and so on. Aye, he found more freedom in a pot of blacking than in doing the polite in any of these editorial offices, so-called. A man's a man for a' that—needs freedom of conscience to get at what's in him. Death o' Little Nell —all the great panorama of his books he found in the freedom of handling a few blacking pots.

"When I think what such fellers would 'a done on the old Ivory—a great revelation of world beauty to a London-bred lad. . . . The growth that comes from the sun . . . but there'd 'a been no Little Nell for the world to weep over.

"Come to London fellers, look at Phil May. A soft London heart that. We learnt boxing from the same professor. Professor Balls, Paradise Street, Lambeth, it was.

"A soft-hearted feller, Phil May.

> Every daisy in the dell,
> Knows my secret, knows it well——

He was in Gurney Street, Walworth, when he was using the words as the motto of the sketch he was doing. Very friendly with the coster girls.

Every daisy in the dell——

My voice is a bit thin to-day. . . .

"We used to go to the robin contests at Greenwich. May's favourite sport. Fighting *or* singing. Covered cages, of course, for a song contest. Robins—they've got a big streak of humanity in them. You may cover 'em up, but they'll battle out with song.

"Aye, London. . . .

"Well, ma'am, talking about London won't write this book we're after. Have you—have you heard anything from the printers yet? Excuse me, I mustn't seem to hurry you. I know what delay there is, once inside an office.

"How did you like my country girls on the ship? I gave 'em homespun to wear. More friendly than fur. Not so barbarous. (That's good, because it's me). Aye, in lasses like these you can surely see the mothers of the race. Mothers o' Lancashire lads. Pioneers o' clog and shawl.

"A bit o' homely thrown in'll always throw up the romantic. But we're leaving the homely behind now —I'm coming to Cæsar himself soon. He's surely in for a bit of a surprise when he falls in with the webbed foots.

"He meant to stay the winter in Britain. *Frigori in hestati,* was it? Pleads the rigour of the winter as an excuse for getting home to Rome. Nay, what he meant was that he was afraid of a severe hiding from the men with webbed feet and hands. Aye! He'd thought to be like the winds and invade the north. *Horrifer invasit Borisus.* But his omnipotence wilted somewhat when he met the web foots.

"Not that the Imperator was one for bombast same as Philip of Spain. Couldn't attack without draping his ships with a lot of church stuff all glistening with jewels. Crucifixes and so forth. I'm going to show this Cæsar to the world a sportsman and a gentleman. Aye, he was that! An enemy no thinking man could afford to despise. And if he didn't roam quite as far west as the old grey gull of Lancashire, or know Africa as I know it, you've got to remember the poor stuff he had to put up with as sailors. Never a sicklier sailor than the Eyetalian! A dago like that'll keep seasick for a week. No notion of battling out for manhood's sake. No doubt seventy-five per cent of Cæsar's fleet were seasick. Having marched through Gaul they wouldn't be feeling too seaworthy.

"An Eyetalian. . . . He'd be sick from Liverpool to New York if you gave him a chance. I've watched 'em on the boats when I've been travelling that way myself. Puny fellers're not used to Atlantic notions of rough weather. Ice-cream fellers like that—they can only drift to the big towns. New York's scented with ice-cream. There's a society in Soho that gets 'em over from Italy and provides for 'em for a few weeks before going on as emigrants to America. Supplies 'em with monkeys and a barrel organ or the wherewithal to buy the ice-cream outfit. But this sort'll never put manhood into any country. I never met a dago riding under the rods.

"Ma'am? Oh, aye, I've walked the tracks. Like this Jack London feller they talk about. I've seen a fair lot of American society riding under the rods. All sorts o' fellers, changing their State for the good of their State. Or a profession for the good of his profession. Law, and so on. Law's always offered too many advantages in the States.

"Aye, the track's full of 'em. Blind baggage and so on. One place you must never get insulted on is on the track. There're times when you must swallow a rock and smile over the stomachache it gives you.

"There's some roughish places in the States. Coldsprings [?]. They used to shoot a judge there every year or two. But you could get whisky any time there none the less.

"Well, ma'am, another finger o' the sun's slipped away. I must be going. There'll be quite a lot to do this week to chase out me notions."

CHAPTER VI

AND now away from all gayment Harrold spoke and all listened he had heard of such booty to be got along the Cornish coast that if they happened on the time and overalled one of these merchant ships he could find Kings Ransoms, as they had tin and gold and dug it from the ground and what, said all, we will hug this Cornish coast as I fore one will nere return home without booty and to this they listened it was wise council, as they were truants all, and all, as sailors say in the same boat. And to this they all agreed and drank mead on it and after shaking hands which was their seal and Sign in those days they changed sail and headed for the Cornish coast. And now between watches they rigged themselves in such like armament as they had Borrowed from the Keeps such as Saxon shields which were small and round shaped and only used with dirk and poynard at which they were clever, and also such games as stick dager which is a dagger thrown from the arm and lights straight upon a mark and thus they spent their time till coasting threw the morning dew they nearly overan a longboat close in on the coast of Cornwall and shoving a ships hook into a rolock hole they pulled the stranger alongside. This of course surprised all hands and laughing the boys would have let the longboat go but seeing something shining that was packed together and was not fish they asked the boatman what it was and being a superstitious man of Cornish breed he answered tin. In those days tin was worth more than silver so the boys being now awakened and alert boarded the long boat, whilst the crew stood agast seeing they were overhalled by a Vyking ship. Harold on being handed up some of the cargo declared it to be of peculiar worth and ordered all of it to be put on board at once and put extra grapples on the longboat. And now appeared a man who seemed to be of forren birth who with arms akimbo resented in loud voyce the removal of his property and received two dirk thrusts in the but and a knock out blow from Harrold's fist which sent him to sleep on the bottom of the long boat. The rest of the men in the boat all stood with hands high as the bars of tin 47 in number were passed over, and from the boats bottom they off loaded 20 bars of copper the whole being worth a kings ransom. And now Harold called on his mate Ogaunt who spoke Gailic better than the rest and held converse with the boats crew who were welch men and were servants or miners of the man who had deighned or dared to gainsay the off loading of the boat. At this the coxswain who was Cornich said, these are but servants of this man who are now loading his ship which lies a little north of us and comes up yearly from Juda and this man who now lays prone is a Phoenician from Jury. And Harold answering with a smile said thow must come along with us and calling to his mates for a flaggon of Fingalls and giving them a large draught each and bidding them to be of good cheer turned them adrift telling them to go back home and sing to the good folks that they had met a vyking and putting the coxswain aboard the Wallrus turned the boat adrift in the thick mist. And now they vered round and droping sail they sped with muffled sweeps towards the direction pointed out. After a while in the mist came a smell of cooking such a pleasant smell, but the Cornish coxswain now half drunk said that was the smell of oil they used, and were now buisy cooking fish for breakfast. They now slowed up and made all ready for boarding as the captive Cornishman had told them she carried men at arms and was a big Phoenician galley owned by a man who was on board and had come to Cornwall for tin, copper, silver and gold all of which were mined at that time by the welch miners (Cornwall at that time was Whales). And now spoke Bill O'gaunt as the Quarry, a big ship all bedisoned with an Emblazoned figure head, loomed up. All ready he said and the good old fashioned answer came aih, aih, Sir. Then with a word to the helmsman (Bows on) he shouted, bowmen aloft. And as the boarding boards fell Harrold wished the armed watch Good morrow from the poop, whilst his second, Bill O'Gaunt spoke in Welsh and asked for the captain of the vessel whilst he bade the frightened men at arms half of them tancoloured, with some Nubian niggers who stood agast at what they thought was an aparition from the sea, to lay down their arms and lay prone which they did quickly and now came rushing from the

Caban the Phoenician Jew the owner of the ship, followed by the captain in command, calling on his men at arms to wake up and defend their ship and master and for his pains the stout son of Abraham was pinned to the deck by an arrow shot from the yards through his right foot and as he was a bad looser he even now called on the armed ships guard to fight, and quickly received a second arrow throw the other foot which left him completely pinned to the deck and motionless whilst a rush forward by some armed Nubian took place who had answered the call for help. These were quickly despatched and fell from an arrow shot like singing music. And now Harrold in loud voice ordered all to ly down who wished to live and jumping on deck with a dozen of his chosen men they passed aboard their ship all arms they gathered from the Foreign ships guard and kicking the ships captain in the ribs, they bade him arise and pay his toll, asking him how he dare sail their seas without permission, and as he was half paralised with fear and was slow to answer they brought him to with a few dirk jabs in the butt. And now being quickened up, he was only too willing to hand out anything he had aboard. Harold first went through the cabin, on the table they found two candles burning in candlesticks of gold which were burning so the captain said to the God of Juda and were solid gold, these they took and likewise discovered fifty bars of tin eighteen of copper and nine small but heavy bars of gold beside a small box of large kerngorms (precious stones yellow coloured found in granite in the mountains of Whales and Scotland). They took away all fancy clothes and blankets, together with fine woven carpets and a stand of arms, some of which, the swords, were inlaid with gold. And now they ordered the frightened Skipper to be lively and hand over the best cargo he had as they were in haste, and they promised to leave him in peace as soon as they had sufficient loot. And this was quickly done, and they were very choicy in their packing. The goods of many varieties were quickly aboard the old Wallrus who looked very ominous especially to the Nubians as every now and then he would bob his head on a wave crest the Nubians atill prone were intent on watching him and wondered what strange unknown power he imparted to the vyking ship. They now entered the galley where they took away the fish which had already been fried in pure olive oil and was good eating. And last of all they passed out ten large flaggons of wine which they sampled and laughingly declared all right and this being passed on board they laughingly declared to the good old Captain they were satisfied but promised to meet him again and next time they visited him they warned him to have his toll ready, as they always charged extra for delay. They now left hurridly and bid all aboard the Phoenician ship better luck. They then dropped sail making all taught with much merriment they sailed away south along the Cornish coast, dropping the good coxswain close to shore they made him presents of value and a small jar of wine, he declared he was well paid and wished the lads all the luck the world had in it. They were overjoyed with their handsome catch which all agreed was a lucky find and in high glee they quaffed the Phoenician wine in celebration of their visit to Cornwall which they would long remember brought them in such a good store of good things. Speeding down the coast as evening drew nigh they sighted the coast round lands end which showed up plainly in the far distance in dark purple shade which made as nice a setting in the all-coloured sunset as one would wish to see.

CONVERSATION.

"You've gone through it, ma'am? If it's facts you're wanting you'll notice that I've given you a fancy picture of a Phœnician ship as they appeared in the dawn of English history. Fiction always carries more weight if based on realities, George Bussey says. That's why you've got to put in the smell of the cooking. Takes a lad's fancy that's far from his home and his mother. I thought of it the other day when I was a bit under the weather. Too cold to reconnoitre these meat tickets they've left me. At my age a modicum of hunger's better than catching a chill. Larger wisdom to stay in bed and fill the fancy with bygone feasts. That caretaker, though, tries to do the decent when I can't cook for meself. Brought me up a cup of that so-called beef-tea you sent down. Very welcome on a morning like yesterday, with old Boreas in such a chilly mood, but below par as an incentive to literature. Somewhat lacking in romance, excuse me. Warms the body but leaves the brain dull.

"That's where the Americans make a mistake. Prohibition's a sound notion applied to bricklayers. Body without brain is what they need. But apply the same notion to poets and other literary figures and it'll be a proper washout.

"American literature's not what it was when Poe was exercising the fancy. All this Jack London stuff —childish notions for a sensible people! Too meagre. Washington Irving, he'd be the one to take his bottle o' port like a gentleman. Romantic fellers like Edwin Booth—recited young Lochinvar to us lads at school —they need the incentive natural to the imagination.

"Aye, 'twould 'a turned American genius sour to have prohibition too soon. . . .

"Prohibition. . . . What a fancy! Why, I've told you before George Washington's own father was a stiller. Aye, he knew the shape of a mash-tub. 'Tis a well-known fact the prohibitionists try to cover up. Plead medicinal purposes and so on on behalf of the father of his country. They're afraid to face the fact that George Washington kept body and soul together by a little good whisky. Nothing more than human. And man enough not to be ashamed of his common humanity.

"I learned a good deal of history from the moonshiners along the Blaauw River there. It means Blue

River. You can see the blue water from the top of the hill. A splash o' water in a landscape'll always soften the heart, whether in nature or the cinema.

"Aye, you put your bottle down and walk away, but you mustn't look back or you'll catch the eye of the revenners. . . .

"Well, ma'am, what did you think of my Phœnician ship giving in straight away? That's how they'd do it. Straight away like an Eyetalian. *Misere cordia,* so to speak.

"I've been seeing this chapter plain for some time back. Waking up early, and so on. Aye, I saw that when the lads left Fingall's Keep they'd have to get in with a Phœnician carrying tin from Barmouth to the Isle of Man. Barmouth, that's where Pritchard Morgan was born. They get silver and copper there to this day. Get me a map, ma'am, and I'll show you the spot. An atlas is always somewhat helpful to the memory.

"Barmouth . . . here it is! And here's Dolgelly . . . we played cricket against those fellers there . . . and here's where we used to go yachting with the father of one of us. . . .

"Oh, aye, they took us all to see the old gold mines and copper mines. Party o' lads from St. Edward's. We went in a coach and four, a pilgrimage to Bedd Gelert's grave. Some o' the fellers spent a lot of money on the homespun stockings. The women sat at the door knitting 'em. Talk about machinery, so called —there nothing like the craft of the fingers! A woman sitting at her own door with her work is one o' the pretty sights—pleases nature herself. What's there to improve the mind in a factory machine? No time for a poor woman to have a pretty thought. 'Tis thought softens the day.

"Aye, the wool at Dolgelly's the finest in the world.

"Pritchard Morgan a poet? No, he was the feller that worked the mines started by the Phœnicians. Sixty years ago it might be. A romantic notion when you take into consideration that the copper used in Solomon's Temple was mined in Wales. Taken there by the Phœnicians. They lived a lot on Mona * and traded down the coast of Wales.

"That's how I saw me picture. You see, they smell cooking and when the dew lifts there's the foreigner not three hundred yards away from 'em. I thought it'd be a natural event to make lads follow the smell o' food. 'Not *kelp,*' says o' Gaunt, sniffing up and down the wind. 'Not kelp. Lads, it's—something to eat!'

"Aye, something to eat, but not likely *they* knew anything about. What they smelt was olive oil. Macaroni and garlic and suchlike Dago vittles being fried in olive oil. A foreign smell that'd tickle the nostrils. However that may be, alien or no alien, one's not too choicey at sea. You can't get your mother's food at sea. It made those lads savage hungry. So I pictured that as soon as the foreign ship stood clear from the dew they were up in the yardarm in two jiffies, and let fly at a big black-haired man parading the deck there in his togs and toga of crimson and blue.

* The Isle of Man.

"Pinned his foot to the deck. All he could do is to shout to his men to bring out the toll. The Phœnicians knew well that when they saw the great figurehead of the walrus they must bring out the toll for the vikings. It was cheaper in the end than having any petty differences about it. They thought no more of it in those days than coming to a toll bar in the highway.

"Aye, the man from Jewry was fairly trapped by the foot there. And when the boat gives a heave on the swell he falls on his back—a most comical apparition. Crucified, you may say, to his own deck. The boys had a good laugh about it while they were turning over the toll and chattering together about the proper wakes * they were having.

"Aye, laughing lads could hit a bumblebee in flight wouldn't make much to-do about nailing a Jew to the deck. The man with the bow, he's *mobile*. What if those boys had brought one of the Roman's vaunted catapults to help them capture the Phœnician? Couldn't 'a done it. Too much bombast about heavy artillery, whether of the present day or in the dawn of history. Come to that, could a sword and a shield

* For the benefit of readers who do not know the north of England it must be explained that "wakes" in this sense is not the same as an Irish tryst by the dead. The wakes is an annual event of very ancient origin which lingers on in many villages. It is a church festival whose date is governed by the saint's day of that particular parish, and the village marks the event by a local fair and fairings, always preceded by a thorough cleansing of the cottages. Scrubbing and scouring goes on for a week before, and much overhauling of Sunday clothes. There are variations from the saint's day rule. For example, one village holds its wakes on the first Sunday after the second snow. One suspects the priest who in mediæval times arranged that of being somewhat of a killjoy.

have helped those lads to the loot as quickly as a flight from the yards?

"Taken all in all, there's nothing in battle to supersede an attack from the bowmen. Three hundred arrows to the minute. Three hundred bows twanging at once—impressive, like any other of nature's music. And for hand fighting, the cutlass! . . .

"As useful and not so cruel as the trident. The best combination for the vikings would 'a been to follow up the flight from the yard with the cutlass when boarding. The trident had a larger reach, but it was unsuited to anything but barbarism.

"A cruel weapon that. Have you ever thought, when you see a penny, that there is emblazoned the very sign and seal of England's greatness on the seas? The trident and net, ma'am—the very weapons, speaking of intimate fighting, the vikings used to overcome all enemies. A cruel thing to flaunt on a coin! Spearing a man and leaving him with three holes poisoned instead of one. A barbarous idea doesn't even up with notions of Christianity. And Victoria's head on the other side!

"Whether the trident and net or Albert the Good's Queen, 'tis only a further manifestation of top dog.

"Aye, the world ought to cutlass the feller preaches top dog. There'll never be peace until we've got him down.

"Mind you, he's never a fighter. Nothing but a Parliamentary, so called. Did Carl Woerman and Hatton and Cookson fight up my rivers? Wasn't Herr Schiff like a father to me? No, ma'am, it's these Parliamentary fellers'll always be poking about with the trident. The traders—aye, and the missionaries—know more about olive branches than the stay at homes. Get out o' London, get out of England!—and you've got the air to expand your lungs. Brotherhood o' man comes easier up those rivers. 'Tis brick walls and too much railway travelling sours the spirit. And when the sun's hidden in the smoke o' factories.

"Aye, there's a lot of top dog on a coin. Put a little picture of Mary and Jesus on it and it'll be a help to civil feelings between the nations. A mother and child'll always take the heart in all languages. Topical, that's what it is.

"I'm not denying, ma'am, that the trident and net made for success in viking days. But 'twas never the king of weapons, like the arrow.

"Mobility's the key word of the vikings, same as of all seasoned fighters. Look at Drake's ships! Nothing more than pigmies waiting for the invincible Armada, so called. Nothing more than pigmies—*but fast sailers.* Only using the oars for turning. And quickened with the spirit of ancestry. . . .

"Swiftness on the sea is as necessary to a man as to a swallow. The vikings knew that, plus the feller who built the catamaran and gives himself to the sea as cosy as a gull sleeping on the waters. If man takes his lessons from nature he'll come to no harm.

"Look at the *Alabama.* Built for swift turning on a

yacht keel. The *Alabama,* built at Birkenhead. She was a syndicate. Always meant for privateering.

"Aye, there was viking knowledge went to the shaping of the *Alabama.* A grand manifestation of Lancashire's friendship with the sea.

"Mobility. . . .

" 'Twas the notion of some lawful privateering roused the Lancashire families to patriotism. It paid 'em to be choicey over the lines and the keel of her.

"Aye, for a seafaring people'd been fed on the Great Exhibition, Crystal Palace and so forth and et cetera, for some years back 'twas like a bit o' nature to turn to the sea again for a bit of profit plus adventure for the young fellers. One of me uncles was killed at Galveston, but he'd had his fling at a bit of natural life.

"That *Alabama*—she could spin round to face her enemies like a wild animal. Swift as a wild cat. The most dangerous boat ever designed. She paid five hundred per cent to the syndicate that owned her. Aye, if the *Kearsage* hadn't been chain armoured. . . .

"Raphael Stemmes was no fighter.

"What's that, ma'am? Nationality? I must be honest and say I never heard it. Jewish forbears seemingly. Whatever stock he came from he was no fighter. When your enemy's chain armoured you've got no chance of survival unless you board her with cutlasses. Stemmes could 'a sailed a boat against the Almighty Himself. But when it came to a fight he was no credit to his syndicate. Some o' me uncles'd 'a done better for their country. Most of 'em were in it. Aye, they'd a' known you can't expect a ship to get up and fight for you! You've got to help her out when she's *in extremis*.

"Off Cherbourg it was. A proper sea duel! With a handful o' cutlasses it might 'a made history for the *Alabama*.

"The two captains'd scraped acquaintance with each other in a Cherbourg inn. They'd challenged each other to the duel. The coast was lined with spectators to see the battle, same as they do for the boat race.

"Not much Oxford and Cambridge fancy notions about a fight like that. 'Twas the death scene of an ocean eagle. Tragedy in a panorama like that.

"Aye, there were tears shed in the yard'd built her when the news came that her wings had been broken. Gentleman of the name of Bolton saved the survivors. Feller with a yacht. Took 'em all to Liverpool. They were flying the Southern flag.

"Aye, more tears shed amongst the craftsmen'd fashioned her than in the parlours of the rich families'd known her only as a filler of the moneybags. There's nothing stultifies the imagination quicker than the counting-house, so called. 'Tis the other feller gets all the fun, the one that's used his head and his vitals to create a thing of beauty—so named by the poets.

"Aye, when you laugh easy you've got to pay for it with cry easy. These counting-house fellers, they'll be blaspheming for a bit of ill luck like the *Alabama* losing herself. Using bloody language whilst the other feller that designed the boat can do nothing more spectacular than wipe away a tear.

"There sure is a vulnerable spot in shipbuilders for the child of his brain, same as nature has provided in a mother. 'Tis another name for the heel of Achilles —same fancy notion as the Greeks had.

"Aye, the man that hasn't got a vulnerable spot is *stultus*. But there's some fellers've got overmuch for comfort and that's the poets. Fellers we used to meet in Evans' Cowyard, as full o' sensibility [sensitiveness] as a young feller going to make his maiden speech in the House. George was a great comfort to the young parliamentaries when he was Master of Hansard. 'Let me down easy, George, for God's sake,' they'd say. Couldn't sleep for thinking of it. Come under his windows in the small hours and ask him to read a bit out to 'em. He'd send 'em away in good spirits, whatever *faux pas* they'd been committing. And being often teetotally drunk they'd not notice the improvements he'd been adding to their speeches for 'em. George never expected young fellers to be as wise as he was, come to Parliamentary matters. They'd go away singing and full o' bombast as a turkey cock.

"The salt of the earth, George Bussey, for young fellers. Nature surely provides men that attract humanity as a salt lick attracts the wild animals for the health's sake. An antidote to sickly philanthropy, like old Jonathan Rider I lived with in Georgia.

"Aye, I was doing a job on a mantlepiece one time for a doctor. Town in Georgia it was. 'Twas one o' those mantlepieces too elaborate to let a fire burn, so I was taking it down to see where the fault lay.

Cold blizzardy weather, and one day when I was slacking off a bit towards dusk in a shack at the back of the house I saw an old feller come out o' the doctor's house looked pretty near the limit for down and out. You know how you feel when you see 'em. And when there's snow and all. . . .

"I'd just had quite a nice fish supper meself. Place down the street where you could get it for fifty cents. I'd a bottle o' moonshine, too, stowed away in a grip, and the doctor'd just paid me something on account for the job. I felt sorry for the old chap, and being one who's always believed that halving your luck's doubling it I called out to him if he couldn't do with a fish supper. And I gave him something to fit himself out with a flannel shirt. He looked as if the wind was clawing right through his bones, and his shoes were gone and sodden with wet. I said if he'd come back after he'd fed we'd spend the evening over a fire and a bottle I'd found covered over for safety in the doctor's wastepaper basket.

"Aye. And in due course of time he comes and sits with me and looks me all over. Said he'd enjoyed the fish supper more than any meal he'd had for years.

" 'That's a nice fire you've got there,' he said, and I told him I'd had to break up one o' the doctor's benches for it, there being nothing else handy to make a fire for a friend. No fire burns bright when you're sitting alone before it.

"Aye. And presently he said he must go, and he thanked me and said it'd been a donkey's years since he'd spent such a pleasant evening. We were talking about the Ogowe River and so forth. But in a few minutes he was back again and the doctor behind him and he said 'That's the chap. There's your moonshine, and there's your bench on the fire.' They both laughed and the doctor introduced me. 'Twas Jonathan Rider, the richest man in Georgia in those days. Owned half the street I'd sent him down to get his supper. Sort of rich man's fancy he had for spending nothing on appearances.

"An old man he was then. A big man in X——. Acres o' cotton fields and turpentine. I went to live with him. Plenty for me to do as overseer on a big estate like that, and he was getting old. Sentry jobs over sundry interests. He had stills on a good many of the islands in the Trinity River.

"Aye, that doctor was submissive. We were good friends later on.

"Well, ma'am, I'm outstaying me welcome altogether to-day. I must get back and twist a bit o' wire and chase an idea I've got for something spectacular. What do you say to those lads tackling the tail of a Roman convoy for loot? Roman wine and other gewgaws they'd never seen before. Luxuries for the Roman camp during the hard season! Bonbons made in Rome. Women's fancy togas and all the fancy face powders of a tottering race. . . .

"You can help me with the women's clothes. There'd be sandals of blue kid and so forth.

"Oh, aye, they brought the women. They meant to

keep house in Britain. Needles and spinning wheels and kitchen pots'd make a viking lad stare.

"Riches at one haul! Those lads'll be finely set up taking it all back to their mothers. They'd know it'll make 'em forget the punishment.

"Of course I'm going to make 'em strictly honourable. One tenth for the chief and a fifth for the commonweal, same as all loot is divided. Strictly moral, commercially speaking, the vikings. Talk about socialism, so called, why a respectable viking settlement had found it all out a thousand years ago. No paupers there. Every one had to pull his weight in the commonweal without any newspaper rant or Sunday night preaching, same as we're favoured with down our way.

"Take what you want and divide it fair's the bedrock of harmony amongst a sensible martial people. Always has been. Where these so-called socialists make a laughable mistake is in thinking they can carry out their notions without a paramount. As soon have an army without a general as do away with the hereditary chiefs. 'Tis when they realise their big mistake and try to replace hereditary paramounts with some pasty, clarkish feller got nothing to him but a fountain pen and a packet of cigarettes that the *mêlée* begins.

"Socialism. . . . What a rumour!

"Come to that, look even at a sensible democracy like America. Always changing the paramount chief by election leads to confusion. A bar to progress. A reigning family's like an idol in a joss house—you know its faults and its physiognomy from generation to generation. If it gets a bit scratched and battered here and there, it's a god none the less and loses no power. But put up a new feller to stare at every few years and there'll always be somebody to see what's missing in him. He hasn't got the same fingerprints and features as the feller before him and that'll be his crime.

"Excuse me keeping you at the gate but when a notion gets started it's somewhat difficult to avoid it.

"There's one thing I forgot to mention: You'll notice that I finished up with a bit of sunset effect this time, but it's only lightly sketched in. A kind of a sample. I thought I'd leave it to you to empty the paint-box on, if you think it needs emphasis. When you're chasing a story you're not too inclined to step aside to do the necessary when you come to a sunset or other panorama of nature. So—if I could leave that to you, ma'am. Being a writer you'll know the *modus vivendi,* so called.

"Aye, thank yer! That's surely a weight off my mind. Now I can get along with the action better if you'll weave in the scenic. There's not too much space for sunsets in my room at present.

"Excuse me calling you back. . . . I've been regretting I didn't put two arrows in that Jew's foot instead o' one. For the cinema you've always got to overdo things a little to meet the demands of *Homo stultus.* Better make it two.

" 'Twas a common way of securing an enemy. Pin 'im with a clothyard arrow to a board or a bench and he's safe. He'll not move away without your permission.

"It's sure take as a cinema. A little water, enough to take a biggish ship, is a sure draw in any picture. Plus the historical spectacle of Cæsar himself. 'Julius Cæsar, sporting gentleman.' That'll attract the English. They understand the importance of it.

"All races become decadent when they leave sport alone. And one of the biggest forms o' sport is looking for a landing spot in an unknown country. Look at the Portuguese! Given over to decadence since they stopped looking for a landing-place in foreign parts.

"Well, ma'am, I shall not turn back again this time to worry you with my notions, but I've got a hint of folk lore for you, perhaps you noticed. I've made those Nubians stare at the figure of the walrus, because naturally they'd take it to be some big voodoo of the conquerors. Some sort of fierce god of another tribe they'd naturally watch with awe. Not knowing the old walrus to be a peaceful denizen of the deep, he'd surely take on a supernatural expression in the eyes of a poor Nubian slave.

"A fine figurehead'll always impress a savage. Aye, it's natural to all men to stare at another feller's totem with distrust. Some o' those sailing-ships coming down the coast—there were plenty of them still in the earlies. Their proud figureheads would sure strike mortal wonder into fellers like my Pangues, sensible as they were.

"Ships . . . there's more relics of religion on ships than there is on land. Come to that, what're figureheads but a solid bit of religion? Totem or patron saint or owner's wife, they've all survived from religious times. 'Twas the Puritans took to putting their wives as figureheads—trying to get away from religion in the world of commerce. But they'd not be able to wash away religious oaths from the lips of sailors by such a common device. 'By Marie, I'll draw a sword on you.' That's how they swore at you in Elizabethan days.

"Aye, Mary's never left the ships, even if it's a Presbyterian. Gods and goddesses'll remain in speech. Even if deprived of their just prayers they'll pop out on an oath when they get the chance.

"Come to religion on ships—didn't the Romans have their household gods on board prior to the Blessed Mary? Nice little ones, handy in size, but not conducive to the spread of Roman mythology in the north.

"The north's always hung back from religion. The vikings were teetotally devoid of gods. That's why they had no trouble at being turned into Catholics. But they never made good ones, being a naturally cautious people. They'd never fit in at New Orleans, where to be Catholic's in the air.

"A happy place, New Orleans. . . .

"The Irish were easier, having a natural relish for the supernatural. Blarneys and so on. The Scotch, too, with their kelpies and what not, were more apt to turn to conversion than the vikings. They'd always been too busy with the sea. The sea keeps men roaming and the feller that roams has to carry his god with him—he'd not be too useful left in a well or a church at home.

"Vikings . . . they looked to the sea for all, good and evil. No superstitions. Nice little article it'd make—the Norseman's lack of religious superstition. . . . You can trace it to the sea, that'll make no terms with any man—except that she's got a softer heart towards the man'll fashion a boat that can be friendly with rough weather.

"Aye, the vikings had no objections to fairydom, but they'd no voodoo. In Lancashire there's byroads and crossroads where boggarts still haunt. I know many such. . . .

"But walking through the woods and so on, when there's spring in a Lancashire glade, you'll feel nothing to arouse superstition, alias fear. The basis of all religion, so called. All the boggarts and blarneys of England don't amount to a shiver. Any little apparition of an English fairy'd cause sincere pleasure. It's when you get to the bloody voodoos of Africa that religious fear gets a hold. The vikings were never troubled with the horrors of Druidom. Too sensible! When you're always busy seizing a living from the sea there's no time to conjure up religious feuds and feelings. Aye, their only religion was the sun, that's why they turned so easily to the older church. Catholicism's always mingled with fairy notions plus the joys of nature.

Where there's a mother and child there can be fairydom but no voodoo.

"Tommy Bamber was great with fairies. He'd always slip in a fairy or two.

"Well—here's to a certain *au revoir*."

CHAPTER VII

THE Wallrus as the little ship was called more than held up her reputation of being the swiftest vessel owned by the vykings of the Faroe Islands as she walsed on the great ocean swells which are generally met with whilst rounding the Lands End. And here a keen look out was kept, as large beacon fires could now and then be seen with figures of strange men moving around who seemed to be signalling. At this these wild Norse lads wondered. They had made no mistake there was surely some great happening amongst these folks ashore. As the Moon rose casting a splendid light over land and ocean they had quite a good view of hills, forests and shore, but still they wondered as they could now see men in motion and more astir than is usual along sleepy coasts and every now and then the sea birds would rise and grumbling at being disturbed send the sounds of their complaints to sea where the lads understanding them being born among them all agreed there were ominous doings. They now stood out to see bearing south west and as the sun threw out his first wave-tipping beams of light they could plainly see the Scilly Islands to the West. And as the sun rose higher they were soon in the midst of great flocks of sea birds as this has always been a homing spot for the seafaring feathered race. After rounding Lands End they kept in shore as much as clear headed sailing would allow and soon with their keen eyes spied fishing boats and sailing close to them they hailed the first one they could. This sailing boat was Captained by an old grey headed Briton who called to them to slow up, the rest of the fishing crew were made up of boys and girls, at this the Norse lads were surprised. The old fisherman now enquired of them whence they came, and on being told they were Vykings from the North he laughed and asked if all the sea robbers from the north were gathering so they could plunder the Romans as was their wont with other folks who travelled the sea. And now they all laughed heartily even the girls joined in eyeing these young sea wolves with gladsome looks. Young Harold now said thow art partly right but tell me why thou asked me such a question, or hast thou seen any of our kinfolks sailing the seas hear abouts. Any ships the old man answered Yea son, they have passed here along the coast, five or six ships whilst our fishing boats which have been on the alert have given news of seeing several other droves far out to sea and they are many and all sailing towards where foreign ships are likely to come and this news I give thee is true. Harrold thanked him for his plain speech, whereupon the old man continued, telling him that one who was wellknown on the south British coast and was a Vyking chief had called on being sygnalled from the big camp near Falmouth and had held converse with the British chief Casballan and after that Casballan had moved his camp and all his warriors and chariotts away down the shore travelling east where they expected the foreigners to come as the coasts here abouts were too forbidding and dangerous on which to land such an army as that which followed Seasar. And all the full grown men from every where had gone with Casballan so that the hamlets contained only old men old women and children, as all the women folks strong of limb and active had as was their ancient Custom in such times gone to share their luck with their men folks. Harrold now gave the old man a few presents from loot taken from the Phonecians and the old aged fisherman was greatly pleased biding him to call on the people camped along the coast who would be sure to give the Sysmacks * a good wellcome, as they were their friends and would be twice welcome in such times as these. The Swift Ship now parted with these good hearted folks, and making all sails taught they bolled merrily along the beautiful coast of south Britain. They passed many fishing boats and small craft which were busily engaged in carrying dried fish and supplies of food to the Camps along the Coast. They passed many of these and towards Evening they were hailed by a boat and asked to stay for a while if they could possibly do so as a British chief and his lady wished to travel with them to a large military camp further up on the Eastern shore. To this they consented, and Harold with one of his sailors went ashore and there met the chief who had hailed them. The camp was situated along the skirting of an oak forest

* Mr. Horn occasionally calls the Norse boys by this name.

near a small village, and here were several hundred of rough looking warriors armed in a great variety of fashions and were most dressed in skins of great variety and most of them carried shields made of toughened hide of several thicknesses tightly bound together by copper rivets, many of their arms were also made of copper. The women folks also were clothed in fur capes and shawls and both men and women were tatoed and wore their long hair braided. There were many sleds and war charriots these latter having copper sythes attached to the Axels. They were a merrie lot and most of them who were of fine build and stature passed the night in singing and dancing to the tune of the Welsh harp and meade drinking. The young Norsemen admired the fine looking horses tethered around the trees. It was early day dawn before the Chief who had been buisy most of the night arranging affairs with his wild-looking officers appeared. Now all were ready to depart on their journey eastwards. As the charriots moved off filled with wild looking warriors the sleds followed, and the rest afoot formed as wild a stream of humanity as ever was seen by mans eye. The Chief with his two sons and wife now boarded the Wallrus and were greatly cheered by the vilage folks who were left behind, whilst the little army could be seen quickly wending its way along shore. As the ship hugged the coast they passed many of these wild bands, whilst once a while they could see small bands of mounted spearmen, and as they sailed swiftly along they often passed villagers waving good luck from the shore. By now the wind freshened and passing by the brow of a hill they saw long lines of charriots and warriors and could plainly hear the songs that they sang and also the harps wild music. The Young Sailors were surprised to see such unacustomed sights and above all they wondered from whence came these bands of warriors who surely if they once could gather would form an army fit to meet Ceasar or anybody else willing to try their metal. Their passengers had been all the day excited especially the fair lady who seemed to know the names of all the marching clans which she would mention to her husband, and no doubt she did as she was of good blood and understood well the meaning of it all. As Evening drew nigh they passed a cliffe upon which were longhaired and bearded men who were ranged around a large stone on the top of which there was a fire burning with bright flames and the fair lady seeing this called to her husband and sons and all bowed their heads as an old man who was in the fire circle held his hands aloft and in the right hand he held a knife reddened on the blade. These holy men were holding sacrifice and the old man with his hands held high was steering a spirit back into its god. At this the boys wondered as all their Gods they knew about came from below even from the bottom of the sea but these holy men made converse with a God above at which they were surprised. And now the whole circle of Druids held their hands on high, and chanted so loudly they well could hear it on the wind and then they all broke off only the one old man who held the knife who spoke in loud words and plaints to something in the sky and on hearing the words which she well understood and holding her chief by the hand the lady bent lower down and never lifted up her long haired head till they were well away around the point of land. A camp larger than any they had passed now came in sight and the chief told them this was his own camp and home, and his name he told them was Casballan. Boats pulled by oars and sail now met them and they asked Harrold if he would come ashore with them as he had important news from Rodger the Bold his father which he would give him once he had seen the messenger himself, and Harrold quickly jumping in the chiefs boat was soon ashore amidst the gentry of Britain who were here in common cause against the Roman attack which they were now well prepared to meet.

CONVERSATION

"Well, ma'am, I'm a bit ahead of Father Time this morning. But don't let me disturb you. Take it in and read it at your leisure while I rest here. . . .

"It surely elevates the soul to get away from the streets. Those villas across on the hill there always remind me of Madeira. Look as if you could see the ocean from them.

"Aye, Sundays're a bit of a trial. I was at mass early this morning and that makes a bit of a getaway for an hour or two. But then when you go back and try to boil your shirt. . . .

"All the fellers that aren't *Homo stultus* wash their shirts on Sunday morning, so it's not too easy to lay your hands on some hot water.

"There was a bit of a *fracas* early this morning too. Those girls that have the ground floor—looks like a little shop and costs double what we pay upstairs—next to our entry. They're demimondes, if the truth be known—set up there a few weeks ago—and a couple of constables came round this morning. Smiled majestically and took two of 'em away. One of 'em had a black plait down to her waist. They wouldn't give her time to do it up. One o' these silly Dutchmen most likely. No imagination, and what follows is no kindly feeling. Aye, a London policeman'd 'a soothed her down. He'd 'a said 'No hurry, miss, you can go and make yourself respectable first' and she'd 'a gone willing with him. No need to bring shame on a girl in the street. In front of a lot of natives, too.

"They're just the same with the natives. No breeding. Give me five hundred o' the London police here on a Sunday instead o' these mannerless fellers, and the whole place'd sure get titivated, *skokiaan* * and all. Even a drunken native can observe if he's spoken to with manners. He'll respond to good feeling and do his best. All these Dutch fellers think of is to get a conviction and ease their natural feelings with a bit o' brutality.

* A forbidden intoxicating drink brewed by the natives.

"What makes London so safe—first and last 'tis a law-abiding place—is because a London constable knows when not to convict. He's brought up to use his judgment and with less time to do it in than a learned judge and jury. No ponderous books to consult for a precedent, so called. The only book he consults is the human record that's writ plain in a face. 'Go,' he says, 'and sin no more.' That's the best bit o' law for a seasoned member of the force to remember. But these young ignorants. . . .

"Never been to London, so what can you expect of their education? If right was right, every member of the colonial police'd have to have his three years in London streets before he'd be turned loose in a place like this. Same as the clergy have to go to these colleges to get etiquette plus the benefices of religion. 'Tis the police that set the standard of Christianity before the prison chaplain can take a turn at preaching repentance to a poor feller.

"Aye. . . .

"Well, ma'am, I mustn't waste your time. 'Tis these Sundays they give you in the Golden City make me somewhat garrulous on Mondays. Does me good to go to mass, though. Aye, I'm not so fond of playing truant as when I was a lad. Summer days . . . they used to feel me head, when I got back from mass, and they'd known I'd been swimming. In winter 'twas our boots were likely to betray us. We used to go shooting rabbits with our bows and arrows. . . .

"There's no gift of nature so kindly as to give back

to a man the picture of his boyhood days. I can easy fetch myself to home sweet home. If you practise you can do it. Get into your dream when you want to.

"Aye, we used to go out shooting in the snow. They'd show up well in the snow. But there was never any slaughter. The bow and arrow gives the rabbits a chance of a bit of sportsmanship. Not like exploding their little bodies with a handful o' shot.

"We used to keep our bowstrings round our middles. Purposes of annealing, same as the vikings' wives had to wear 'em and sleep in 'em. A bowman'll always keep his cords supple. In those days an enemy was always in mind. Look at the dumb bells they had to use for strengthening the pull of the right arm! Regular training they had to have. Heavy bells with the clappers taken out or muffled—hold 'em out at arm's length and so on to increase the muscle.

"Aye, Yorkshire won on the arrow. George Stanley refused to fight. 'Where's George Stanley?' King Richard said. Dick the Devil. All humpbacks have a devil hidden somewhere. Compensation o' nature, that'll devise a means of defence for the weakest. So she makes the humpbacks strong. Look at the buffalo, nature's humpback. A morose feller'll attack you for pleasure.

" 'Where's George?' he says. And his men-at-arms said 'He tarrieth, sire.' Tarrieth? *He never came.* Aye, that was why Lancashire. . . .

"Why, yes, ma'am, if the doctor could spare me a pipeful. But I've got me own matches to-day.

"Well, ma'am, how do you think it's weaving out? I've had to push in a few of the other sex to embellish the picture somewhat. Those girls fishing, and the chief's wife. A woman like that'd look well in the cinema—plait of fair hair down to her ankles. Silver brooches and a lot o' dignity. There's me contrast with the fisher girls. She was one of the gentry of England. A grand lot, taken all in all. That's why I've had to show her religious feelings. 'Tis the gentry and the church've welded England together for good.

"The feller that never feels like dropping a thankful prayer or two's *Homo stultus*. These fellers that can't embrace Christianity because they don't believe in a few miracles—what a rumour! Miracles! A big ball spinning in space, and man with the privilege of balancing his life out on it, that's miracle enough for me. I'm not asking the Almighty for anything more intimate. I'm not expecting the Ruler of the Universe to cure my toothache as proof that he exists.

"Even the vikings felt that miracles were vouchsafed to them when the sun burst forth for so short a time and poured out all the rejoicing and benefits a man could possibly have, even to the flowers. In the north there's a proper furore of delight when the sun appears again. The flowers give better honey. It's yet to be proved that they're without sensibilities. . . .

"Labrador and Greenland, the best honey in the world.

" 'Tis from the burst of sunshine the vikings got their restless notions. Everything in flight—the bees and the birds—no pleasure in staying at home. The sea was their element, but 'twas the warming sun called 'em to get out the ships. Sprung from the walrus, as they were, what else could you expect but a return of energy when the sun came back?

"Is it chance that gave us a walrus as ancestor? Nature plays strange pranks we can't account for. The webbed man of the north—you could prove by reversion where *he* came from. You could make your name famous all over the world by *that* theory. The web-foot children exist to prove it. Is nature playing pranks? Well, she's played 'em all her life. And that's something we must get used to. If it's theory you're wanting, quite as feasible, to my mind, as the Taungs' skull. Why, I heard Dr. Ballé [Ballay?] say that there's a portion of the ape's skull'll never catch up man. Isn't that proof we never sprang from him?

"The ape's a dirty thing to spring from. I'm an old hunter and it doesn't appeal to me as an appetising solution. Lord Kelvin says that man is older than the monkey by some thousands of years. Pointing that the monkey is the spring-off of some degenerate branch of *Homo genus*. Who's to say they're not the leavings of some colony of imbeciles and lunatics got out of hand? I've seen those scientifics on the Ivory Coast examine the brain of a gorilla and they said it had faults and failings resembling the brain of a lunatic.

"Aye, nature! Whether ape or walrus, one big result of her experiments is man. Look at the northern races and see what intelligence there is there. If you were to tell Lord Stanley he'd sprung from a monkey, he'd, as like as not, say 'You'd better do the same, my lad,' and give you your congé on the jaw.

"Look at Lord X——, the paramount chief of Catholicism. One o' the richest men in England. But he's Catholic first. No gentleman'll ever wear his moneybags on his sleeve. Leave that to the little fellers never sprang from a walrus. Sired by a desk out of a ledger. The moneybag's their only reference [approach] to a family crest.

"Aye, a Catholic gentleman'll wear his church on his shield still, same as the Crusaders. That's why we're getting stronger. Drop all your church pride, same as the newer parties do—excuse me, I know your leanings—and you'll go down. The man who flaunts his church in the face of the world is flourishing a sword. All these little agnostics, so called, they'll never make much to-do in the world. The feller that writes *stultus* on his banner'll never gather an army.

"Come to Catholicism. . . . The *crux crucis* of the whole matter is not the imaginary flimflam of the English Church but a solid basis on superstition. Otherwise human nature. Catholicism is based on a thorough grounding in the needs of humanity. And one o' these needs is not to try and trade on both sides of the river. Reformation's all well and good if you're strong enough to follow one bank only; it's when you come to hankering over trade on the other side that you weaken your position.

"Look at Newman. He'd got to make his choice and

he turned his back on the so-called freedom of the Church of England. 'One step enough for me,' he says. He took that step. 'Twas over to Rome.

"Then there's Manning. He didn't like no man's land any better than Newman did. Excuse me mentioning it, but I suppose you've heard of Manning? Mannings o' Liverpool? Princes of commerce they were. Not being Lancashire yourself I thought you mightn't have come across the name. Well, being of commercial instinct, he naturally didn't suffer in the heart as Newman did. But as a man of business habits he saw that there was more security on the old bank. So he crosses over.

"Not but what I'm just as near your church as the Catholics—cut out the foolishness of both sides. . . .

[Mr. Horn was afraid he had been going too far to be quite courteous, hence this hastily devised counsel of perfection.]

"This Reformation, so called. All a matter of poppycock! Henry and his grand books and learned ideas *re* religion. . . . And what was his life? The Reformation was nothing more than a getaway from a hot corner he'd got himself into. Holy matrimony with Anne Boleyn was what he'd a fancy for. And when he got her 'twas a bad thing for England. Perhaps he had fewer paramours after he got interested in religion, but the restriction only caused a reaction. Made him burn in other directions—knocking Virgins to pieces in the churches and so on. Burning and shouting. . . .

"What an apparition to support the Protestant

Church, so called! 'Tis not to be wondered at that it almost tottered a bit, stout though he was. Reformers. . . . John Knox wasn't much better, although he kept his hands off a plurality of wives. Kept 'em at bay by a stern demeanour. But he killed a lot of people in his religious furores. Molten lead and so forth. The Scotch have always been a bit coarse in their notions. Look at Macaulay for a historian. Criticising the popes! Talking about the line of the popes. [?] . . .

"Aye, but Catholicism is something you can't down. . . .

"There's never been any religious body, from the Druids downwards, haven't had their moments of mistake, come to that.

"How d'you like my Druid scene? It'll make a dandy cinema, properly thought out as a spectacle. But best seen at a distance, as this chief's lady saw it. But these cinema fellers'll not consider that. No money in restraint for them. They'll bring the victim near and pour blood all over the picture, owing to being somewhat lacking in literary manners. There's breeding necessary in painting a picture of historical times, same as there is when you take your seat in Parliament or enter a lady's house. Breeding'll always leave something to the imagination.

"George Bussey knew the etiquette of Parliament, if any man did. He had all the privileges of the House. Could walk in with his hat on. Have his drink same as a member, and go to sleep if necessary during a speech.

"Aye, Parliament . . . nothing shows the decay of manners more shockingly than the so-called Parliamentary procedure of to-day. It's these underbred little fellers from the underworld. Think they can run England on socialism. Haven't we flourished for fifteen hundred years without it?

"Think they can seize manners and privileges they've never used the sword to obtain. 'Tis not money and a busy tongue've brought the Duke of Norfolk his prestige. 'Twas the fighting habits of his ancestors. Top dog never stood on a moneybag for long. The body of his enemy was always safer standing-ground for a gentleman. That's how the ducal houses arose and that's how it'll have to be in the ultimate.

"Aye, George. . . .

"I used to do odd jobs for him. Take dictation during a debate. A proper father to us young 'uns. Dickens had been his friend when he was younger. They'd known what it was to be where we were. Poverty Square's a bigger welding force than freemasonry. The masons're bound by their comforts. Banquets and so forth. Regalia, so called, and other bombast. But an empty pocket'll always call other fellers to share its fortunes.

"Aye, there's kindness in London. 'Tis in the air. Not like the Golden City, where kindness is all newspaper rant. All save and except the sort o' fellers come to our house. They'll listen to you, even if they do sell a bottle to buy a bit of breakfast now and then. I'm not forgetting there's charity here. But can I unburden my ideas to a party brings me candles and soap? They don't want to listen. . . .

"In London there's kind hearts in every street. 'Tis that makes you want to go back and risk the dirty skies. Look at Evans' Cowyard. Belonged to Jack Kipling o' Walworth. The King of the Costermongers. Had a fried-fish shop where they smoked haddocks. A wealthy feller, that! Had a place near Nobby Clarke's, the hat shop, near Lambeth Palace.

"*'Isn't it a nobby one, in just the latest style?'* That's where the word came from—old Nobby Clarke, that had a hat shop near Lambeth Palace. . . .

"Aye, Jack Kipling was a proper Londoner. He let us sleep in Evans' Cowyard. If a feller was a bit out in his accounts, he could always go and bed down in the cows' straw. Clean, mind you!—Kipling treated you like a gentleman.

"Chevalier often slept there. And May, when things were dark for him. . . .

"The—the New Cut, Lambeth! *That's* where it was. . . . And there was a feller named Bodger had a bear he kept there. Dancing bear. He kept those two fellers sometimes. Made it dance in the streets in his free time when he wasn't due at Ignett's Circus.* Introduce the bear to big houses round Pimlico and make it do fierce antics beyond the bounds of what a dancing bear should do. They'd be given a shilling or a half a crown to take it away quick. Ladies screaming and shutting the windows. Children running, and so

* Is this possibly Ginnet's?

forth. May and Chevalier'd give their assistance in the performance. Laughing fellers they were. They'd easy make enough for a pint and a shave and a bit of hot supper.

"Aye, Evans' Cowyard . . . Jem Mace slept there too. Did boxing turns at Ignett's Circus. Why, you'd meet poets at Evans' Cowyard. Kipling'd always advance a shilling to a feller, and naturally that was a sure place to find 'em.

"Holloway the quack sold his pills round about there at a penny the box. Top hat and a sort of travelling coach to lecture from. Lambeth, that was, before he became a rich feller.

"The Baroness Burdett-Coutts knew Jack Kipling. That woman had a heart for animals. Known as the donkeys' friend. Built good stables for the costers' donkeys. A millionaire, but a good woman.

"Well, ma'am, I'm getting a bit talkative. I mustn't forget to tell you what is in my mind for these lads to do next. I told you they're going to attack Cæsar's guardship. Get that and they'll be free to raid the whole convoy. Of course they'll have to consult the wiseman first. There was always a deal thought of the wisemen in those days. Even the Romans couldn't do without specialists. The vikings, too, without the expense of temples for the oracle carried wisdom around with 'em.

"Aye, you'll see when they're going to attack the Roman galleys they'll have to ask Bill the Wiseman to take a look at the weather overnight to see if propitious. 'Twill be one o' those sunsets like you see in Lancashire when the sky and the sea've been like a palette —orange and a fine duck-egg green spilled over with streams o' crimson lake and india ink. And over where the hunter's moon is you'll see black streaks o' cloud and one right across the face of the moon. And if the moon is in D, as they say, and has tilt enough to hang a jerkin on, 'tis a good omen. But still better when a black arrow lies across her. . . .

"I shall make the wiseman point to the arrow that's got its tip towards Britain. One o' the most favourable omens you could have. And before long there'll be half a gale blowing across the Channel. Just what was necessary—the Romans being sickly sailors. But being very noble gentlemen, they'll throw themselves into the sea rather than to surrender to the arrows of death coming in a flight from the yards—bewildering 'em like birds dashing in your face when you're cliff-nesting. . . .

"Aye. . . .

"But I must leave you to do the necessary *re* sunsets, et cetera. I'm getting a bit old to go off at a tangent like that. At my age weaving the plot is what occupies the mind. I'd always rather watch a sunset than put it into words. Less meagre—watching is.

"There's a picture I'm running into the next chapter'll bring up the interest into top speed. I think I told you I'm making imperial Cæsar stand on the poop, toga and so on, with a scroll in his hand. *That bit o' parchment's a map o' the world!*

"Well, naturally he'd have to have his map on board

for reference. What he didn't know was that it was the most ignorant map ever drawn, and that's an ascertained fact. A square map of the world! What a rumour! Nature loves the globular, and that's why she made our world the same shape as a dewdrop or a soap bubble floating through space. If you want fancy notions, I can give 'em to you, and there's one.

"The sages of Rome were a densely ignorant lot to have sent him off with a map'd mislead any child. Why, they'd allowed for no geography at all up in the far north! And here were these lads coming from a country had no official existence, to attack the world-famous Julius Cæsar. Sporting gentleman though he was, he was naturally ignorant as a babe where the map was concerned.

" 'Where do these lads come from,' he says. And there was no one to tell him except a Danish galley slave at the sweeps. 'They live where the sun goes down into the sea.' And he said it was a half year's journey to their home in the north, but you couldn't get back within the year. And Cæsar being naturally curious about these wild men with their great hairy chests and webbed hands unrolls his square map of the world and said he would prove the Dane a liar. He said there was no such place ever been thought of even in Rome where all the best sages were.

" 'The sages of Rome will laugh thee to scorn,' he said. 'Tell me further of these wild fellers,' he says. 'Are they Nubians? Have they tails? Are they perchance feathered as well? Thou hast lost thy head, slave. Prate not to me of webbed men!' He shows the poor slave the map and points to the north where there was no geography at all and laughed him to scorn. 'These webbed men'd slip off the world if they were to adventure so far as thou sayest,' he said. But the slave tells him they can live without geography, being at all times masters of the sea and being independent of land if necessary.

"Cæsar jumped up immediately. 'No land!' he says —'then where do they live?' He laughed. But the Dane looks at him as one gentleman at another and tells him all the portents o' the north—the sun that's still red at midnight on a summer night and the northern lights that hang like a fine spangled curtain across the world and guard the palace o' Boreas and the massive stores of ice that trickle down to keep the world moist and cool and free from putrefaction. And Cæsar's notary takes notes on his tablets and reads it aloud to the generals and they all laughed at the slave. They were finely tickled at the notion of such fancy doings in the sky.

"The great Imperator had to take instructions from a man of the north, poor slave though he was. You'd always find a Norseman amongst the galley slaves! No doubt an uncrowned head amongst those dagoes and Nubians.

"Aye . . . I can hear that feller whistling to imitate the blackbird and what not. Keeping up their spirits before the sun came skimming the wave tops at daybreak. . . . The language of nature's one that's understood by all men. Who knows but what she designed it for that end—keeps 'em together a bit in spite o' religion. War and so on. . . .

"Nature'll sure outlast the Tower of Babel. There's no doubt but what the linnet and the thrush'll enjoy the last word. And it's a word understood by every man that's ever been a boy. Aye, when every Frenchman's dead that ever wasted his country's chances on an African river the gorilla'll still be sending out the dawn cry that spells the language o' fear. Dago or viking, it's a language that makes 'em draw together in full understanding of the natural ties of man.

"Gorillas! . . . What agitates the spine of a youngster when he hears it is something he doesn't understand. Same as if he heard a roar from a madhouse when he's passing by.

"That Dane'd be a big feller, too, bringing the small stature of the Emperor into relief. Small of stature plus poor sailors, it sure needed an Emperor to lead the Romans to the attack of Britain.

"Fair and handsome we'll make the Danish slave. Aye, and he'll not wince when Julius Cæsar laughs at his notions *re* geography. A big feller'll always keep his dignity. The black-eyed man'll always drop his gaze before the blue-eyed. And that's a fact well known in Scotland Yard. In the front offices you'll always find the blue-eyed men.

"Aye, they'll look at each other, Dane and Roman. . . . It'll make a good bit of juxtaposition to make 'em slave and Emperor.

"The positions are transposed somewhat at the present day. The north's top dog. Nature never gives out a breed twice. She'll not turn back to ancient Rome for a pattern—not even if it were Cæsar himself! If a man dies out he's not one to make a copy of. 'Tis the viking that's still strong in the blood. And while Lancashire lasts England'll not go under to another race.

"Aye! If the old families o' Lancashire knew how King George was kowtowing to the League of Nations, so-called, they'd batter his head in. If it's come to that, better fight it out with the world, and go under like gentlemen. Be done with it!

"Well, ma'am, it's better not to get on to politics. When will politics stop? Never. Not until I'm dead, or elsewhere."

CHAPTER VIII

HARROLD was now conducted to a large stone hamlet with a spacious hall and was there introduced to some of the South Britains, mighty chiefs and warriors, who looked well in their warlike trappings. And now a steaming bowl of hot mead was carried in and served in horns of silver whilst the clank of arms played never ending music as the steaming mead was passed round one bowl after another with no let up. Here Harrold laughed as he thought the Saxons were the limit in drinking especially when supping mulled ale, but they were not in it with the Britains when drinking hot spiced mead, which really he thought as he tried it was second to nothing drinkable for good taste and refreshment. In fact the whole of this camp was one continual round of Jollity, and but for the Surity that they were collected here for war purposes one would have thought that this great band of armed tatoed barbarians had met for merriment only. Suddenly the whole camp was astir with the knews that Ceasars troops were reported all aboard the galleys and making their way up the French coast towards the narrows of the Channel where they had intended to cross over to Britain. The camp was now astir and the Hall was now nearly deserted. Casballan gave the News to Harrold that his father had Ceasars camp watched and had sent a despatch saying Ceasars forces were in two halves. The first portion of his fleet contained his fighting men and he himself was in the large galley which had sails of purple whilst his baggage and supplies were coming later in the second section, and would make sail as soon as they had the word that he had made a landing that was safe from further attack. And as the sea was not too rough for sailing (the Romans were poor sailors on heavy seas) he could be expected to reach the British coast about sunrise. Casballan now bad the lad to thank his father for his kindly act which they (the Britons) could never forget and biding him good morrow and the best of luck Casballan quickly left with his aids and fighting chiefs and the great band of men were soon on the march to meet the invaders. Harrold now returned to his ship, and gave the good news to his crew who were now in high glee at the thought of being able to tell their folks they had seen Ceasers landing. In fact they were all so excited that these boys, brought up and many of them born at sea, knew nothing but the wild rocks and valleys of the Faroes really had seen nothing of the worlds grand sights. And all agreed to leave the British coast and meet these Romans, and being children of a warlike race, who looked on dame fortune as their only guide, they now quickly left the British coast and sailing swiftly towards the Narrows of the Channel they ran up more sail, flying Jibs and topsail, making the Old Vyking ship spead like a hungry sea bird. They now strung their strong bows using the strings which were worn round their shoulders which kept them in good trim and gave them extra strength, and making all ready for a fight if necessary. Whilst Ogaunt the navigator cried, "What ho all if I dont have an arrow at this great man Seasar, I will take the next best man." "And I and I and I" ran through the crased lads. Whilst they were buisy trimming up one anothers locks and Dressing up as was their morning custom a voice rang out from aloft Sail A'hoy. Not one but many and such large ships it must be some mighty man. Surely these are the Romans. The lads now quickly climed to their positions aloft whilst Harold standing high on the stern deck told off all the rest to their posts. As the Roman fleet came in sight they had not long to wait before they saw a mighty ship on the large poop of which stood many men clad in different garments from the others these, no doubt [were leaders] especially the one foremost of the rest who held up a parchment and pointed towards the British coast. They now drew swiftly up and Agreed One and all to cross his bows and take one good look at this man who seemed to be the One Man of the world. This was a foolish move, and for their pains as they were within long bow shot the Cattapults of which these boys knew nothing opened up but as the shooting luckily was bad they received no harm and answered with an arrow flight from the yards and several men fell on the poop of the Roman ship, close to where Ceasar stood, but he seemed to notice nothing and as the boys afterwards said he has good nerve this leader of the Romans. Still not satisfied these lads now agreed to cross his bows again but not to shoot till they were fired on, as they would get their own back on the men who fired the machine which carried rocks and stones. They now turned and gathering speed they made a short curve swiftly at arrow range and this time away went one of their boarding boards smashed in splinters another shot now carried away the flying Jib whilst the Old Wallrus figure head was knocked fairly well to one side by some ponderous mistle. But the Norse men had got their own back as many men fell to deck being arrow-shot around the Cattapult. And still the one erect figure stood motionless and smiling, and as the lads sailed away, they doffed their woolf skin Caps and cheered Ceasar lustily and the Roman commander being a gentleman warrior and sport bowed in recognition and thous around him did the same whilst the boys still cheered him as they sailed away. A loud answer came from the Roman soldiers and all cheered these plucky lads who had dared to exchange shots with the great Ceasar on the high sea. And now the general in chief asked who were these people and whence they came but no one seemed to know till a galley slave who had seen the hapening from the deck said he could tell his Officer who they were and he was brought before Ceasar. He declared they were Vykings who came far away from a land of Ice called Iceland where they lived on the rocky shore amongst the Sea Birds, and wandered the high seas in summer North South East and West and his countrymen called them sea wolves, and such they really were for like the wolf although you could see only one ship there were always many. Continuing he said some of them were born with webed feet and hands like a duck and could swim and dive and live in the Water like seals and fish. And here Ceaser dismissed the man laughing heartily at such ignorance, and all smiled as the poor slave retired. And the general still smiling said no more. Especially as the Coast of Britain was well in sight but Calling all his generals around him his Admiral now formed the fleet in line ready for landing.

CONVERSATION

"Well, ma'am, I've just come from Father O'—— He's going to sign a paper'll get me hospital treatment. A thorough-paced gentleman. No church in his conversation. Above par. Looked at me for a few minutes, puts his hand down and gave me ten shillings. No orthodoxy, you understand, to come between the man and the priest in his make-up.

"Aye, he looked at me. . . . 'Tis a heartening thing when you spend your days in a lodging-house to meet the eye of a gentleman. He knew me, although a stranger. 'Tis the confessional teaches 'em to read the heart. If he hadn't had a cent in his pocket I should 'a come out a better man for that look he gave me. Not like that stock exchange feller picked my brains the other day for half a crown: He'll make thousands out of that little bit o' knowledge I gave him. Finest coal in the world and nobody tapping it on account of a disagreeable climate makes a feller rely on squareface.

Half a crown, and a sneer growing in his face before I reached the door!

"Aye, there's meat and drink in the look a man gives you when you're down and out or there's poison. And to-day I've had a notable feast for the soul from that priest. You can forget these office fellers're after mineral knowledge when you meet a gentleman.

"It takes a gentleman to recognise another of the breed. And I'm one. Aye, you know it ma'am! Before ever I told you about the fist and spear you knew I'd got history in me veins. That's what it is! History. . . .

"An old bridge near Frea had the Horn coat of arms emblazoned on it in stone. That's history! Something that's beyond the ken of these office fellers in the Golden City. And look at the Horn chalice! Belonged to my brother that's a priest one time. 'Twas lost at the general *mêlée* at the Reformation. A good many of the Horns have died for the old religion one way and another. And one of 'em must have had great faith in the natural kindness of man. More than that he was justified in his belief . . . the chalice got back to the old fist and spear a couple of centuries or thereabouts after the big turn-up so called the Reformation. It got back because it said underneath it . . . 'twas scratched in Latin . . . 'Please take me back to the Horns' o' Frea'. Gold inside and silver out it was.

"Aye, if that chalice could voice its wanderings there's no knowing what strange secrets of history could be added to the sum of human knowledge. The Reformation was none too popular in Lancashire. It was up against old English itself there. What a German monk thinks on religious matters can have little or no sway there. I don't know anything about the make-up of our human nature. That's known to Providence alone. But that old Horn sure got at some unborn heart with his hasty cry from a fugitive man.

"Well, ma'am, you'd oblige me by reading this bit o' manuscript. Take it inside, excuse me for suggesting it. Oh, aye, I've got me pipe here, but I've had no tobacco for a couple of days. There's always fellers need a chew or a pipeful. . . .

"That'll be ample. I'll excuse you now while you read it over. Take your time over it, there's no haste. . . .

"You got the picture ma'am? What did you think of the lads' first attempt at a sea fight? Of course I could 'a made it more elaborate if I'd waited till they'd found their fathers' fleet and all attacked together. I could 'a drawn you a fine study of viking tactics . . . but it wouldn't 'a been in the proper tangent for the book. 'Tis the lads' adventure this time. Touches the heart to think o' laughing lads sending an arrow at Julius Cæsar . . . such an impression as he made on the known world. Having a bit o' fun with a fight. Like boys in the snow. . . .

"As a cinema spectacle I could've given you a dandy if I'd brought in the fathers as well. Bring in the fathers and have a regular sea fight. I'd make 'em draw a human net in two lines. Crescent shape, and close it at the ends. Sure's a spider's web, and that's the formation used by practised vikings to catch an enemy. A proper clewline [?] . . . draws the net into a bag round the enemy. Give me your pencil, ma'am, and I can show you how we did it. . . .

"There you are, roughly speaking. . . . The enemy's in the middle, and I've given the vikings oars. Looks peculiar, but they were proper scientists at sea warfare.

"Aye, and didn't they use the viking tactics again when it came to saving England from the Armada? Look at the Spanish attack on English sea power . . . all those dark little ugly boats waiting to demonstrate viking tactics of sea brain against wealth and bulk. Waiting to give 'em a round robin that'd sting 'em to death like bees on a fine horse. . . . Bunching together like Indians against the cowpuncher patrol. . . .

"Why, 'twas the viking legend destroyed the Armada, so-called invincible. 'Twas the webfoots fighting for us in the brains of English sailors . . . teaching 'em the half-moon formation and other notable folk lore of a fighting race'd always been friendly with the sea.

"Excuse my admiration of the Protestant side. It's always been hard for a Lancashire man of the old church to navigate his way through the pages of history without mishap to his principles. Conjure Elizabeth on to the biggest galleon of Spain spreading her peacock nature over all and sundry and 'twould be an easy getaway for your conscience. A more suitable place for her to be than goddess of good Lancashire seamen in their little black ships. . . . And King Philip at Hampton Palace wedding his avaricious nature to the noted greed of the Virgin Queen. . . . Easy then to remain true to the dictates of religion. Fight the Armada and the apostate Elizabeth in one action.

" 'Tis the webfoot overcome the religious fancies of Lancashire men. If a feller can show a good fight and handle a boat like nature they'll not ask him too intimately where he says his prayers.

"Prayer's a luxury made safe for the world by the world's fighters. Aye, 'tis war brings out the manhood of the churches, Catholic or Protestant, and proclaims 'em brothers that've always lived quarrelsome when obeying the dictates of religion. And the last bit of religion on earth'll be when two fellers of opposite notions *re* Christianity join in an attack on an enemy and feel love between 'em.

"All those little black boats full of the knowledge of the sea. . . . And swimming down on 'em like swans scorning a water hen the galleons of Spain. . . .

"All the sheen of the Adriatic upon them. Blue waters of foreign parts (better get that down in case I forget it again: 'All the sheen of the Adriatic upon them.' You can use it to touch up a descriptive passage of Cæsar's fleet if I get a bit tired of the high lights). Silken sails shimmering in the wind and the sparkle o' good brass—a vision of wealth and riches casting a religious eye on England's greatness.

"Aye, Elizabeth and those other rough girls so-called maids of honour took the papers from the Cardinal they caught on one of the galleons. That noted apostate—quite a young woman too, and unmarried

—made him strip to his stockings before her. The jewelled cross she snatched from him is still lost. Being a thing of rare beauty it roused her greed. The rest of the baubles she distributed to the ladies in waiting. They say she took a switch and gave him three slaps on his naked skin—she was never one for too much modesty, Elizabeth. Aye, those girls derided him as he walked away. He'd brought an important document from Ferdinand and Isabella—or it might have been Philip. Names get visionary at this age. The documents were to prove that Britain was a gift to Rome. 'Twas meant for the eye of the pope naturally. But they never reckoned on the English Catholics fighting against Spain!

"Come to that, the Catholics of England'll always sack religion come to a question of country. Who's to blame them? There's always a fine bodyguard round the old religion at headquarters in the Vatican'll save it for all time. But the Vatican couldn't save England. The pope himself couldn't save Lancashire from an enemy armed to the *cap-à-pie*.

"Aye, make your country safe for whatever religion you happen to undertake and then fly your holy flag, whether the cross or the crescent. Where a feller finds a safe camping-ground then's the time to light the fire for a bit of comfort and meditation. But it shouldn't be for too long. Doesn't the dawn come every day calling you to move on? No camp should last forever. And that's where civilization makes the mistake of its life, trying to cage the natural man. Trying to make him a stationary object behind bars. Did the great Onlooker give us the world plus the ocean to entice the thoughts of the roamer if he meant us to stay in one spot?

"Massive silver . . . Turkish carpets and so on. All the luxuries of the *haut ton* are neither more or less than neckirons to a slave. And, what's worse, they make heaven itself into the image of a cage. Why, the Son of Mary Himself couldn't stand too much of the synagogue. He liked a splash of water like any one else. Always down at the lake staring and thinking. Consider the lilies, he said. But the religioners've put no lilies in heaven. Common fellers. No blue water to catch the sky. Only gold.

"A golden heaven. . . . And why is that but because of their own empty moneybags? Men've never had the pluck of a louse to go looking for gold. Fighting the rocks for it and watching where the hares'll play to know where the diamonds're hidden.* Aye, there's more amusement in looking and finding than ever there was in keeping. Look and find, but have a good laugh at the notion of keeping. That makes a more amusing heaven than any religioner could conjure up.

"Look at my sister Florence's house. There's something stationary for you. Always the same when I turned up from me travels. Full o' magpie tricks—saying this and that. Although kind to the poor, that were never turned away.

"There's a *modus vivendi* in England that you must

* Warmth is an indication of diamond pipes, and hares choose the warmest ground for their gambols and siestas.

absolutely follow. Especially if your sister's an old maid. I was the only one o' the family that'd seen the world or undertaken the upset of marriage and children. So I must 'a seemed a bit wild to all at home. Me brothers priests and me sisters—Florence was the spinster to the life, but Catherine became a sister of charity.

"If *she'd* been at home—it might 'a been different. . . . More notions of the hearth about a sister that's trained to gentle thoughts of wanderers, whether in the family or not. She'd always a softer heart, Catherine. She could 'a been a wild lass herself if she hadn't thrown herself for safety on the bosom of the church.

"Aye, those northern shipping families always have a wild one or two to contend with. And there's no niche for 'em in the world as there used to be, save and except the church. *She's* not turning her back. The church can take the wild 'uns and weave 'em into goodness. Better than staying at home in the drawing-room—arranging fancy gewgaws every day while the world goes on. Or being a J. P.,* and so on. Flower shows and a bit o' shooting at tame creatures you've reared for the purpose.

"Aye, the prodigal brother's not having such a welcome as the prodigal son. Immediately I smoke a cigar the servants'd be rung for to sweep up the ashes falling on the carpet. And me beautiful gifts of nature from the coast—put into the attic as soon as me back was turned. A bit o' woolwork done by herself or some

* Justice of the Peace.

other cold spinster meant more to her in the ultimate than a bright bird of a bit of ivory carved by a simple savage, or a moidore from a wreck. Proper links with the world of reality—and they had to be hidden away so's my sister could go on thinking the world was like her drawing-room.

"Relations! . . . One of the biggest delusions in the known world. When you leave home you leave brothers and sisters. Flesh and blood. But you've only got to return now and then from the world's horizons to find them a mirage. You think you see a hearth burning. But when you get there. . . .

" 'Tis only a mother can kindle the flame for a roamer. And that's why the church holds power'll never be broken. She provides a hearth that's like a feller's dreams. No mirage there. There's a Child that'll never be grown up. And a Mother that's the same as when you were a lad . . .

"Mute criticism! . . . The most killing thing in the world. Not the biggest warrior'll stand against it. Looking at your tie or your boots. . . . Staring at the cut o' your coat. . . .

"Dumb criticism's the brother of sarcasm. The sarcastical mind spoils all the beauty o' nature, whether in poet, general, or any other feller. But when a woman cherishes it 'tis an outrage on nature that planned her to be a mother. Aye, and the schoolmaster that flaunts it for a weapon in front o' tender lads is no better than a murderer. He's killing the natural belief in man's goodness has been imbibed at a mother's breast.

"I can diagnose the sarcastic in two words—no gentleman. St. Edward's always said 'Come out with it! Be human but be a gentleman.' A professor that wasn't that wouldn't a' been kept there for a week.

"That's a faculty you can't erode by contact with riches or poverty. The behaviour of a gentleman may've lost a race or two but it's never broken a heart.

"One thing about the House of Commons in George Bussey's day—scorn, contempt, or any other political emotion—the dictum was 'Be a gentleman while in the service of your country.' Aye, it'd take more than a bit of generosity to make 'em forget that. George used to say you've got to see a man in his cups before you can estimate the depths of his breeding.

"No man had fuller experience of *Homo politicus* than George. Being Master of Hansard gave him a notable insight into the frailties of Parliamentary notorieties—in those days nothing worse than drink. There was a lot of deep drinking in the lobby then. In my opinion 'twas ultimately better for English prestige than all this tea and socialism 'on the terrace,' as they say. 'Tis better to listen to the dictates of a gentleman under the influences of wine than to fill your ear with the common talk of some feller from nowhere suffering from chronic sobriety.

"However drunk they may have been when speaking in Parliament, George always give it the hallmark of temperance when it appeared in print. The newspapers relied on him for that. The *Times* and so on.

"Aye, even when he'd not been in the house himself

he could tell by the style of the speech we handed in to him whose it was and in what condition it had been delivered. A gentleman could always drink in those days without bringing the attention of teetotals and other commoners upon him.

"All save and except the family circle, so called. The eye of a sister, especially when she's no knowledge of the world through holy matrimony, is apt to be too full o' condemnation. But what can you expect when a woman seals herself up in a house? Brick walls and etiquette never expanded any soul that ever breathed.

"Look at Lucy-Vega—come to women as such. The breath o' freedom sure filled her nostrils, widowed though she was.

"Aye, the Vega-Lucy. . . .

"That was a grand country of pines. Pine woods. Thousands of acres of 'em. And every one to be cut down for the uses of man. Growing there in a state of innocence before the so-called utilitarian appeared on the scene. . . .

"Who's to know what plants are thinking? A feller that's watched a primrose enjoying the airs of spring in a Lancashire glade and seen the flower carnivores stretch out for a kill—well, of course, he knows. No need for the scientifics to display their discoveries before him. And what I'm telling you, ma'am, is that there was ample proof of vegetable happiness in those fine plantations of the Vega-Lucy.

"Look at the quietness below there—very favourable for the intercepting of natural feelings. Nature sending up her fountains of sap into millions of trees—it's not likely they'll receive her benefice without a sign of life. Look at the silence there. . . . And on windy days a roar overhead like the sea itself. Aye, they taste life when the wind passes over! . . .

"Lucy-Vega was the woman that estate was called after. A widow, who started a sawmill. Very fond of the trees she was, but she'd cut 'em down without any sentiments suitable to ladies. Always for action. Always planning for law and order like a man. 'Twas her own energy brought her a fortune. Used to ride all over the plantations with a six-shooter. Seven hundred slaves she had—and every one came back to her after the war.

"When I saw her she was that old. . . . Like a piece of mahogany. I saw her at Jonathan Rider's. She was just such another piece of humanity. Aye, they understood each other, come to managing trees and slaves. She'd known his wife too. *She* knew why the old man went on living at the little shack he first brought his wife to—long after she was dead. 'Stead o' the fine new house built with his millions. Kept her grave like a veritable garden o' posies and a nigger doing nothing but trim the flower garden round the little house. Mrs. Rider'd had a large affection for flowers and when she was gone he kept them blooming for her case she might be missing them.

"Lucy Vega. . . .

"She used to say there was only one way to make money out o' timber. Cut it yourself. Raft it yourself. Have few overseers. Some good horses and a loaded pistol—she thought more o' them than o' any overseer.

"But her slaves all came back to her, and she never sacked a white man for bad temper. Used to tell him to come another day.

"Her chief hobby was bossing up niggers. Riding around through the pines. Twenty thousand acres, and through it that woman rode with her big horse and her six-shooter. . . . They never knew when they'd be seeing her apparition between the trees. The needles deadened sound and she'd not always keep to the fire belts. Aye, they never knew when they'd hear her. . . . 'Hey, nigger! How much you got out this week?'

"But they all went back to her. . . .

"Full o' fire for living, that woman. Like virgin soil. Anything'd grow in a brain like hers. That's why nature prolonged her activities—because she'd always useful thoughts to think. She'd solved the grand solution. . . .

"A rich woman too. Owned a bank. All those trees—and tar-heel camps for turpentine and resin.

"You tap the trees three years for turps. When the tree is cut the stumps're drawn and fires started. In the grand ashes you sow your crops o' cotton and corn. American soil's always eager for growth. . . .

"You'd see her rafts starting down the river. Two million feet o' timber. Great rafts going down quiet to the sea with that woman's trees destined for all markets of the world.

"She'd go down to New Orleans with the rafts.

'Twas her thinking time o' the year. There's no gainsaying the peace of a fine flowing river. It'd bring thoughts o' serenity to any one not *Homo stultus*. Serenity plus the notion that you're going somewhere else on the bosom o' deep water. Going to the sea. . . .

"That woman sure felt the sea calling her when she went down with the timber. Ships and the sea're what were always in her mind. When the rafts got down to New Orleans she'd go and stare her fill at the shipping. You'd think she was an idle dreamer when she got away from timber.

"She'd watch the sailing-ships breasting the blue. Nosing for the horizon. . . . And if one came sailing in from the ocean she'd not go about her business until she'd had her fill o' staring at it. Banks and everything else. . . . Shops. . . . She'd not stir.

"I painted a picture for her. Gave her the choice of a subject. . . . 'Twas a ship in full sail. I made her a barquentine and she was finely set up with it.

"Aye, sail. . . .

"On a calm day you can see a barquentine look like a pagoda in a picture. An apparition of beauty and grey like the stones. Referring to me paintbox I should say india ink could get it with a weaving-in of Chinese white. But simple chalk'd be nearer for softness.

"New Orleans. . . . A busy town when the rafts arrive. Cotton or anything else. The cotton makes a fine stir. Windjammers from Liverpool waiting for 'em. Fellers that know who you are, or perhaps knew your father or your grandfather. Old-timers under sail. . . .

"The *Vega-Lucy's* named after her. Aye, there's freedom in the States for those that value it.

"They're kind in the South, I met a woman who gave me a bed because her grandfather was a Liverpool man. 'That place,' she called it, 'down the Mississippi. The way the cotton goes.' Knew no more o' Liverpool than that. But she'd been brought up to honour a Lancashire man even if her geography was somewhat scanty. She looked at me when I told where I came from same as if I'd been a myth or a legend. 'Liverpool?' she said. 'Come in.'

"Aye, there's hearths open to Lancashire up and down the world that'd be closed to England.

"They'll trust an Englishman in the South. Cross the Mason-Dixon line and you must change your habit of thought. You will not have to draw Abraham Lincoln any more for a living once across the Mason-Dixon. Your pencil'll take a natural leaning towards Jeff Davis.

"That feller sure was the god of the moonshiners. I procured a nice sketch of him once from a lady. Lived in St. Ignatius Square and owned a cotton mill. I gave it as a keepsake to the moonshiners.

"Aye, they made a song about him once was all the rage one time . . .

> They hanged Jeff Davis on a sour apple tree
> But his soul goes marching on. . . .

"My voice is not what it could be, excuse me, but the sentiments surely appeal to a roamer like me.

"Aye. . . . My Greatuncle Ralph had property in St. Ignatius Square. Him that had a house in Hyde Park.

"The last of the buccaneers, that's what my Uncle Ralph was. And a very good listener. Very seldom said anything, but he'd go away laughing and shaking and saying nothing.

"Always had interests in the South. But who's to blame him for keeping a morganatic wife and family there when holy matrimony in Hyde Park'd never brought the blessing of children? He was a laughing man, and he needed amusement. There's no amusement in massive silver when the house has got no more signs of life than a clock's tick can conjure up. Blinds drawn for fear o' the carpets if ever the sun ventured to look in.

"There's sun in Savannah. Aye! And the children clustering round for presents from London. . . .

"An old-style viking, me greatuncle Ralph. He asked his father for two ships to go privateering, but his father said no, one'd be enough if properly rigged out for warfare. So he manned him a ship out. Cutlasses and so on. Nice little cannon. . . .

" 'Twas no more than setting a lad up in office, as they do nowadays. I'll lay there's many an office full o' plate glass and little typewriters [stenographers] that's as good at thieving as me uncle Ralph. And no manliness to show for it by way of gain. The sea'll not let a man degenerate as the city does. Even if he does maintain a plurality of wives, he'll be not less the man for that.

"Whatever would my auntie in Hyde Park've said if she'd known she'd got a wife-in-law in the South? . . . Set all sail, and off to a wife that *was* a wife. Children jumping around . . . nice hot sky. . . .

"Aye, the sun wants us all to be happy. 'Tis easy to forget London. . . ."

CHAPTER IX

WHILST a second line of ships had now with warps and transport cast anchor about nine galley lengths behind the first line of fighting ships the young vykings had found a cave close to where the druids were still making sacrifices and filling the air with their plaintive chants. Whilst one half of their number stayed by the Walruss the rest of the lads climed the cliff so that they had a full view of the landing which took place on a sandy easy shelving beach. They were not alone for quite a number of youths and tattoed girls had already climed the cliff anxious to see the strangers who were about to land bent on the capture of their country which except for internal fueds had been at peace with the rest of the world from time immemoriel. Nor could these simple people understand why a race of people who were so wealthy as to own such a vast number of beautiful ships should come to their comparatively poor home for no reason whatever except it was shere wickedness, but as they told the vyking lads, these Romans would not be long before they would be sorry that they ever gave battle to their chief Casballan who had never been defeated. A distance from high tide mark lay piles of flotsam and behind this crowded a long line of British warriors ready to attack the invaders whilst in the tree clumps further from the beach were war charriots waiting also for the signal to attack, whilst behind these could be seen the Old Warrior Chief and his aids on horseback, intently watching seasars fleet. Some time elapsed before the Romans were ready, whilst trumpets sounded and troops moved around on bord the galleys which were anchored in shore. It was a grand sight for the young folks. Seasars galley especially with its furled purple sails and high poop and its decks now full of armed men clad in glistening armour, made a beautiful tableau. Now all was quiet for a few moments then following a loud blast of bugles the troops began their landing jumping from the gangways into the sea armpit deep in the swells. They endeavoured to form into line which move was rendered extremely difficult as many of them were swept off their feet by the receding waves and had to be helped gain their feet by their comrades. Tired out by this difficult exercise they reached the higher level of the beach undisturbed. Now was Casballans chance to gain a point from Ceasar. At a shrill sound from the cunning old warrior a host of war charriots armed with copper sythes on their axels now bore down on the invaders and so sudden and unexpected was this attack that the Roman line was completely broken. Following this, the savage tatooed Brittons rose from the flotsam pyle and hurled themselves with such force against the broken line of the enemy that they swept them back into deep water with such heavy losses that things began to look ominous for Ceasar. Undaunted by this defeat the romans continued to pore out their warriors from the galleys only to be thrown back by the deadly attack of the war charriots and savage attacks from the Britons. The Norse boys on the crag as well as the native onlookers became so excited that they rose and lustily cheered the Brittons whilst the druids chanted their loudest. Seasar might land they thought but conquer Casballan much less Britain was only a Roman rumor. And quite a long while these attacks and counter attacks took place. The receding tide now gave the Romans a better opportunity for landing and this ceasar took advantage of. From the second line of galleys now poured a fresh army chosen of old seasoned troops. Ceasars last hope of ever securing a landing was placed on this reserve. Although they suffered heavily they managed to retain their formation and although they were forced to fall back the Britons now half exhausted gradually fell back towards the forest which extended for miles along the southern shores of Britain and which Casballan well knew Ceasar would never dare enter. Behind this last army Chore came sappers and miners who were now buisily engaged digging trenches driving stakes and making a fortified camp. At this kind of work the Romans were adepts, so that they soon had a fortified camp which would at least save the Roman prestege and the Reputation of the till now undefeated Ceasar. At this juncture the young crew of the Walruss decided to sail away and if possible find their fathers as no doubt there would be a good chance for loot in the wake of a defeated Ceasar. As they left the headland they were treated to a grand sight the druid dance. These long gowned old men were supporting a large mistletoe hoop through which the smoke from the sacrificial fire ascended whilst they danced the circular Dance of victory to music of harps, now full of mellody now of defiance, and this song now resounded through the valleys even to Casballans camp deriding and challenging the Romans had they but understood their meaning. This put the finishing touch on the grandest days outing the lads had ever expected to have, and making all taught they sailed away as happy as young seagulls on their first flight. The watch was told off whilst the rest of the crew turned tired, after taking a farwell view of seasars fleet and the battle still raging towards the woods. Ever and anon the druid song of victory to the twang of the harps would strike their ears being bourne along by the land breeze. The youngsters were soon asleep and in dreams seeing the glistening Roman Eagles being trampled underfoot by charging charriots and the fighting on the sea.

CONVERSATION

"Well, ma'am, I'm getting along towards anti-climax in this chapter. Saving the climax proper for me finish, when those lads board their own fathers' ship. I'm going to make young Harold attack a ship for loot. He'll be getting frightened now about what his mother'll say. She'd be naturally a bit anxious, but he'll know she won't be cross with him if he takes her plenty of useful loot. Some bits o' bright silk and a few handkerchiefs as well as fancy cooking-pots from the kitchens of Rome.

"Aye, it'll be the twilight of early dawn. He'll hear the rattling of the ship's tackle in the freshening breeze. He puts up his grapples all right when they've stolen near enough. But when he gets over—you have a running-board to board the ship—it'll be his own father! There'll be the lads caught in the net like salmon. . . . Ma'am? Well, the net that's always spread to catch the boarding party. I've explained to you before about the net. Combined with the trident the most efficient weapon in the earlies of history.

"They'll have a good laugh when they hold the lantern close and make out the tattoo mark on Harold's arm—mermaid and crescent moon. Chief Roger's family crest.

"A good job it's his own father. It provides something the young boys'll laugh at and the old men like to read. It'll tickle 'em to think of a son boarding his own father's ship. Hung up in the nets for a bit to give him a sharp lesson not to be so daring.

"Like netted fish they look. . . .

"There were trout and salmon too in the Lune. . . .

"We lads used to know everything in those days. We picked up a deal o' knowledge from old Sil. He did nothing but catch eels. They gave him a little right [freehold] of his own, about an acre. It ran alongside the river Lune. He got more money for eels that came from the Lune.

"Aye, there was a sparkling flavour to that old river! Full o' trout and salmon and running under stone bridges. Those old stone bridges—fairly built on the bones of history and barnacled with time. . . . Same as old Sil. . . . Nobody knew his age. We lads thought he was about a hundred. He used to mend a few nets. The first feller that taught me how to catch a trout by fuddling him.* He'd catch anything in water. Tell you what bait to use for salmon and everything else. He'd tell you where the Hodder came in. And if the salmon were running he could get them when nobody else could.

"Aye, he'd no city tricks. Never been in a city. Nature's child unspoilt. The young ladies fishing loved him. He'd tell them all the tricks of the salmon. The best in the land used to go and see old Sil. . . .

"Everything in that river was game. The Lune. . . . An eight-span bridge at Lancaster. Everything game in the river and I could throw a line as well as old Sil. . . .

"Aye, I've often been jealous of old Sil. Sitting down there on the edge of the bed listening to *Homo stultus* telling you how he sold a bottle to a native, I've sometimes wished my ultimate heritage to lie alongside the Lune. And some lads to respect me, same as we respected old Sil.

"They'd perhaps respect me for my elephants and gorillas, same as we did for his pheasants and hares. . . .

* A poacher's trick of dazing the fish by lime in the water.

"He'd show you how to throw a cricket out on top o' the water. As soon as it hits the water the line disappears but the cricket floats.

"Fishing! . . .

"He had free access to the woods too. Badger's Wood where he showed us how to shoot pigeons. Did you know that wood pigeons are bigger when they're young than when they're old? Stock doves, some call 'em.

"Aye, he never went short. He was fond o' lads. He liked us to visit him. He'd lived alone for fifty years. Lost his wife and child on a boat on the Wye when he was a young man. She'd gone out rowing with some young chap. No one ever knew what happened. They never came back and the boat was never found. Silas his full name was.

"A regular historian, old Sil. He kept the mythologies of Lancashire from being forgotten. A proper authority on the old days. Lingard kept the papers but 'twas fellers like old Sil had all the facts.

"Aye, when men never see a book to cloy the mind with the written word their memories grow sharp with use. But Lingard was a fair-minded man, for all his documents. Not born one-sided like that feller Hume.

"I told you Lingard lived at Hornby. Hornby, where me cousin was priest. There's relics of Mary Stuart somewhere there. Howard o' Glossop gave 'em. The Howards and the Peters won't have a Stanley in the family any more. Not since George Stanley held back his men from Richard. 'Where's George,' says the king.

And there was no reply and no clattering of troops. . . .

"I seem to be chattering like Crane. Feller in Sleepy Hollow. . . .

"An ancient river, the Lune. It knows all the miles of fishermen from the days o' the vikings. . . . Why, John o' Gaunt might've fished in it as a lad, same as we did. I've seen a picture of John o' Gaunt. A thin feller, but strong. Could pull a clothyard arrow to beat any William Tell, and less operatic bombast about it. The clothyard was the length of an arrow. Or you could measure the stretch of your two arms thrown out from the chest.

"Aye, when I see the little fellers measuring lady's ribbons with an arrow length. . . . What a semblance o' manhood he's dwindled to! The measure of an arrow, and he uses it for such a womanish purpose! . . .

"That picture belongs to St. Edward's College, but it's kept at Hornby. I've told you who lived there—the first English historian. Lingard by name. Same house where my cousin was priest. Manuscripts and documents, old seals—all the treasures of history he had to keep an eye on. But not one of these clutch-'em-tight fellers, for all his learned riches. He always gave orders that if any man of letters should come along the pike he was to be made free of the manuscripts and suitably entertained. Glass o' sherry and so on. But nothing to be moved. Between gentlemen the sherry'd be to gloss over the fact that the documents were being watched.

"Elizabeth's seal—that's there. Written with a strong

hand to condemn her cousin to death. What's the woman like that could keep her hand from dithering * over such a murder? If she'd confined her history making to the sea, she'd 'a been a finer Queen. A proper pirate, that girl, but 'twas jealousy that belittled her. Those ringletted lovers that rode after Mary—Elizabeth knew they'd never approach her except by royal command. Even a Queen likes to be made a choice of once in a lifetime, so-called virgin though she be. In love 'tis the female instinct to surrender, and that's what Elizabeth was never requested to do.

"Bold and cruel she was. I've seen the chemise and other fine lingerie poor Mary handed over to her gaolers. Everything she stood up in, poor lady, when she was cast into prison for being a beauty and an attraction to the opposite sex. A proper Queen!

"There was a feller Bosworth Elizabeth would 'a liked for his power over the fair sex. Not a Scot—he was a forester, lived round about the Trough o' Bolland and hunted in the woods. But she had to make the best of Darnley. Nothing better than a spindle-shanked nobleman! He pulled on his hose and became King of Scotland, and so forth, but he was proud to be Elizabeth's lover all the same. She had to raise him to a kingdom—'twould never 'a done for the Queen of England to be light o' love to a common Scotch nobleman. Mary surely had better judgment in the choice of a lover, although fond of change. Bosworth was a fine-looking outlaw'd bring pride to any woman's eyes.

* Old English, as Mr. Horn would say, for shaking.

"Aye, history. . . . If you want history, Lingard's is still the most authentical. They'll take it at Oxford even now before anybody else's. There's a reversion to his ideas going on at Oxford now, Lingard being an Oxford man himself. Oxford's always been partial at heart to the older church.

"There's script and parchment of his in Lancashire that'll show you the history of England. My cousin who is a priest has them.

"Aye, old Sil. . . . There was nothing you could 'a told him about poaching, even if he did hold a bit of freehold. Poaching's like nature. Freehold or not, 'tis natural to all men to want something that's over the border.

"My Uncle Eustace used to have a sympathy with poachers. Always gave 'em a fair chance. Singlestick or fists, whichever they'd prefer. He always gave 'em a gentleman's chance of combat if he found them up to mischief with the game or too intimate with the river.

"Him that killed his brother in a friendly bout. He'd give the thief a chance to prove his manhood. But they'd as soon go before the magistrate as stand up to a feller his height. Old though he was they feared him. Great power in the arms and shoulders until he died.

"He died in his bed by accident. Set his whiskers on fire and couldn't make himself heard, being a bit infirm at that great age. Set himself on fire from always using paper spills to light his pipe instead of matches.

"The softest hearted feller. . . . Shot and drank a

lot. But he kept his remorseful sufferings to himself, and that's why they stayed with him till death.

"Cousin Bob saw him first. . . . 'Is that you, Bob,' he said. 'I'm finished. 'Twas the spill did it.'

"Very soft to animals. There was an old racehorse of his called Juan. They were like mates together. And when he could ride no more he had a hole knocked in the wall and turned the next room into a stable for the horse. Juan could nose his head through. . . . They wanted to be near each other.

"My Uncle Eustace'd listen to my stories. Eighty-odd and he'd never be tired of a bit of adventure in his ears. Roaming was somewhat after his own heart if only he could 'a let go of remorse. Nature never meant man to harbour regrets, any more than she gave remorse to a leopard or an elephant. No progress in remorse, Christian though it may be.

"Over six feet and very reticent. . . .

"A proper landlord. . . .

" 'Twould 'a done him good to strike out from his family. Always wanting to give advice, and so forth, families. More freedom in the States. He could 'a lived like Jonathan Rider and forgotten all his troubles of remorse. A strong feller like that, he'd have had a happy life, only let himself go free. . . .

"No strangers wanted at Jonathan Rider's. No peddlers safe. A preaching feller peddling Bibles was shot dead once. No religion there. A Bible's a curiosity people only have in the parlour for a keepsake.

"Well—with fifty stills to be considered, strangers were surely an inconvenience.

"But he was respected, Jonathan Rider. If he wanted to release one of his friends from prison there were no sheriff'd be able to stop him. Albeit he was good to any one he'd trust. Many a poor feller he's rallied round him. Give 'em a shake down and their vittles and drink and in return they'd act as sentry for him.

"Aye, America was easier those days. When I was living at X—— I'd order a mule-load o' pine logs and under the wood I'd find me jar of whisky. A dollar and a half for four bottles o' moonshine. 'Twould cause a furore to-day at such a price.

"Prohibition has sure been a blessing in disguise.

"The moonshiners went teetotally back on the brewers. Well, of course their worst enemies were the brewers! Who should vote for prohibition if not the mash-tub fellers? And now by the exercise of a little judicion they're capitalists. I've no patience for the unlettered feller that runs down capitalists. The capitalist by what he earns is giving direct labour to smaller men. Labour and money. I earned good money building mash-tubs.

"Aye, prohibition has been a certain benefice. It helped the moonshiner to civilisation. Stopped him from being a dangerous fighter. Gave him some status. When a feller's got status he's not so ready to fight. From his private still he conjured up an education for his children. Now, instead o' making war he buys a motor-car for his daughter. Does a bit of improving travel for self and family. Europe, the Colosseum, and so on.

"Aye, the taste of Americans has teetotally changed owing to prohibition. It made the moonshiner rich and he can afford to support English trade by wearing wool instead o' jeans. Prohibition in America sure spelt a bit o' luck for England.

"But the States can never again be what they were in a state of innocence, when whisky was put out as a decoration to the table and ladies and gentlemen didn't have to commit the sin of hiding a bottle. No better than these Zulu lads on a Sunday. . . .

"Aye, looked at soberly prohibition's brought no more happiness to the world than the apple Eve snatched in the orchard. Every man'll sure look at his neighbour as if he was naked. No curb at all now on morality—all running around to buy aprons.

"And who brought all this morality into the country? 'Twas the bootlegger. Not the old ladies and the clergy—they saw no money in it till they were shown. 'Twas the bootlegger chased the idea.

"That old mountaineer of the South. . . . He needn't sell his corn now. He turns it all to good advantage in a mash-tub. His cousin the sheriff, he'll stand in too with him for friendliness. A tremendous ring. Steel magnates' daughters'll put their allowances in it. Four hundred and so on—they're all in it, either as consumers or producers. Or writing newspaper stuff pays 'em well. Condemning hypocrisy and so on.

"Looked at from all sides prohibition sure spells

prosperity. Greatest good to the greatest number—what more can be expected from it than that?

"Look at Jonathan Rider, come to that. Deceivers of reveners or not, he was well thought of by all. Didn't the chain gang cry for him to buy them?

"There'd been trouble in the chain gang at Trinity River and Jonathan went down with a posse to stop it. He always got slaves from Trinity River. You'd see him looking for lurking devil,* same as they did in Gaboon fifty years ago. Jonathan employed an old slave to detect it for him. A barbarous spectacle, men in chains! Bloodhounds sniffing about and so on. When they saw him all the niggers started crying 'Please buy me, Mr Rider! Please buy me!' He had the repute of being a good master. 'Twas a regular chorus.

"Slaves to the State—convicts, as we should say here. It was the custom for folk to take them on the cotton fields, you understand, and pay the State for them.

"What with one begging him and another, he took the whole ten. But being a bit of an eccentric, nothing must please him but he must have ten jennies too. 'Bring me ten jennies,' he says to the overseer. And before the day was out he'd married them all off, two and two like Noah. 'Now,' he says, 'I'll give you the third of the cotton and a fourth of the corn as if you were a white man. But every eighteen months I must see me increase from every man jack of you. Those're me terms.' 'What in-

* There is a description in Mr. Horn's first book of the fault in a slave which, detected by an expression in the eye, makes him to be avoided by the buyer. The faculty of detecting it seems to have gone over to America with the first slaves and remained in the Southern States.

crease is that, sir,' says the ringleader. All the nigger couples smiling round Jonathan. . . . 'What increase, you black fool!' he shouts. 'Children! Nigger children'll grow up and multiply my cotton. And see it's done without offence to me satisfaction.'

"Aye, his bark was harsh but he'd got a softer bite than most men. Built himself a fine house for the looks of it, but he'd never sleep anywhere but in the little shack his wife had lived and died in.

"Eccentric about money too. Didn't believe in banks for the preservation of wealth. He kept all his title deeds and documents in a safe beside the bed and a couple of six-shooters ready for the inquisitive. When I was living there 'twas my job to sleep with the safe and the guns, being a much younger man, and a better shot than most.

"He got rich in a number of ways, did Jonathan. Sawmills. And he had a bar at ——, was a sure investment. When prohibition came in he invited the outlaws to supply moonshine for his bar. A versatile feller!

" 'Twas the war upset us. I was very happy at Jonathan's and my son had come to give a hand on the estate pending another job. But the war broke out so he had his last job in Mesopotamia. . . .

"I got over meself in the *Rochdale*. New Orleans she sailed from. They gave us champagne and cheered us. . . . Landed at Hastings with sugar. Me cousin got me on to a mine-sweeper. The best he could do, seemingly. . . .

"The most unsatisfactory war that ever was. This

keep-your-distance sort of fighting never satisfied anybody but the office fellers. There was murmuring about it in Lancashire. Aye, when Jutland was posted up there was nearly a riot amongst the women. Clog and shawl've naturally got no patience with scientific warfare, so called. Nothing less than prowess is what they believe in. If those rough girls could 'a caught hold o' Jellicoe they'd 'a torn the little feller to shreds.

"This fighting the unseen is the curse of manhood. Battleaxe and plunder—that's the battlecry of the primitive world. More manly thrill to it than all your bombing in cold blood from an innocent sky.

"Aye, the intimate wrestling of big men for a little matter of life or death was a proper expression of nature. Not like some poor feller caught all alone in a burst o' shrapnel over in France there. Not a friend nor an enemy to give him a touch of humanity in his last hours. . . .

"Fighting the unseen is surely the curse of the modern world, so called. Better die with a man bending over you with your blood on his axe than staring at an empty sky above you. That's what breaks a man's nerve—not to get at grips with something human! 'Twill be the end of all civilization. Eliminate the human from your fighting and you become no more than a machine wound up to express brutality.

"Look at these poor shellshocks. Such pitiful fellers would never 'a been found wandering about the world if we'd kept to the arrow. Even the cutlass is a more merciful weapon than all this elaborate artillery.

Aye, it leaves a feller sane to his last breath, as his Maker meant him to be.

"Talk of intimate fighting, you've only got to look at the *Alabama*. Her captain was no fighter. Raphael Stemmes his name was. Too taken up with his tactics to hitch on and fight it out with cutlasses. No fighter, land or sea, can afford to be enamoured of his tactics. The only tactics you can stick to is to be ready for a quick change. In the ultimate tactics must fall before what's natural, and that's a man behind a cutlass. A man's a man, and none the less so for being armed with an intimate weapon. Catapult or heavy artillery, it's brute force against the thinking animal. And that's what the viking was—*a mobile thinker.*

"A yacht keel, she had. . . . All me uncles and cousins in it. . . .

"Lancashire's always had a strong hand in water fighting. Separate the viking from the water and he'll deteriorate like a hooked fish. Aye, he'll look as dull as a trout on the pantry shelf, all the painted pearliness fading out of him. 'Tis the element nature planned for him, as she planned it for the walrus and the seal he sprang from.

"Why, there's a twenty-one foot tide in Lancashire. One o' the highest in the world. 'Twas a gift of God to the old vikings. Ensured an easy landing. . . .

"Aye, and beyond the water's edge—look at Lancashire! The history of England in concentration. 'Tis well known that what Lancashire thinks goes. Whether in commerce or in the making of the future. If it hadn't been for Lancashire there'd 'a been enemies through the gate. Look at Cromwell. Lancashire said 'We've nothing against you, but come no further.' And he didn't even remember to take his coat off the peg when he went.

"There's a place in one of those five keeps on which it says 'Come not uninvited.' That's Lancashire. But they let Prince Charlie through because they knew he'd never get out. 'There's a bird caught,' they said.

"A good-looking feller, that. But he made the mistake of his life loitering at Preston. There'd 'a been fewer Scotchmen's heads making the clover grow in those parts if he'd got into the saddle a bit sooner. Some bonny lass o' Lancashire, no doubt, working for her country's good same as Judith.

"Handsome folk, the Stuarts. If Lancashire had so willed it they could 'a been the reigning monarchs of England to-day. 'Twould be merry England, but I doubt what other empire there'd 'a been. Nothing like the Hanovers for top dog. But England would 'a lost all her illicit gains conjured up by Elizabeth if the Stuarts had remained top dog. Elizabeth always went off her head at the sight of business she'd never seen. Began to have powerful fancies about what England might be missing if she wasn't always on the sea.

" 'Twas the sombre riches of the Aramada inflamed her natural avarice. Organised piracy she'd always a tender spot for. But we'd never 'a kept the commercial advantages seized by that woman if the Stuarts had been paramount for long. We had to get somebody calm, so we sent for the Prince of Orange. Otherwise the Stuarts'd still be romancing on the throne. Always more interested in romance than the exchequer. . . .

"The Hanovers are good traders, albeit somewhat lacking in wildness. What with the exhibition, Albert the Good, and so on . . . *Flos floris,* as Victoria thought him. . . .

"Well, naturally Lancashire'd no use for a Stuart, handsome though he was. Up in the north you don't get immorality. Lancashire's a pure spot compared with the Elephant and Castle. Or Westminster. The best rents in London there. . . .

"Aye, when it comes to viking country there's a different wind blows over it. I don't know if there was ever anything against even Richard the Third, come to that. Dick the Devil, so called. A proper crookshank, but pure where women're concerned, that feller.

"Aye, I like knowing history that other people don't know anything about. Me uncles knew a lot of hidden history. Book o' Days and so on. And Tommy Bamber, the last of the chroniclers'd keep us well informed. Winter nights and so on.

"Isn't it all such things added together that made Shakespeare? Things that were told him—nothing more. Chiefly the monks, but no doubt he kept the busy side of his ear open when in London. Used to go loafing about the inns there listening to the ideas of gentlemen.

"This William Stanley * you were telling me about. It'd be a natural thing if *he* were partners with Shakespeare. Being in tourage with educated folk like the Stanleys—adherents of the older church—he'd be useful to a feller whose father was nothing but a butcher. It'd suit Stanley too. Not daring to say things openly about the Queen, he'd be able to weave his political notions into his writings. That's what gentlemen always did before Parliament became strong enough for open criticism of the sovereign, same as it was in Victoria's day.

"A notable leveller, Parliament. . . . They'd mix like costermongers, those fellers in committee. A bit of a scrap over some church and state affair there might be sometimes in the committee rooms. But always genial, weeping drunk, some of them. But a gentleman in his cups is no less a gentleman.

"Well, ma'am, I've been wandering from the point somewhat, what with one thing and another. What do you think of my attack on Britain, now you've read it? I could've drawn it out somewhat, the ways these fellers do who write scenes from history. But 'twould be no better for it. Short and sharp's the word for battle literature, especially when you're making a landing through enemy lines.

* I had once mentioned to Mr. Horn my belief that the only possible person to have written Shakespeare, if Shakespeare himself must be ruled out, was the literary and courtly Sir William Stanley, a much more humanly possible and less coldly classical candidate for the honour than Bacon. Being attracted, I imagine, by the idea of a Stanley coming to one more well-deserved honour, my colleague listened with less disdain and impatience than I had anticipated.

"I ought to 'a put in something about the stature of the Romans. Naturally the boys wondered how such small men could fight so well in formation. It's a bad drawback to be small when you're wading through surf. I slipped in the chariots and so on, but the physique of the Romans escaped me. Small stature and bad sailors, only a grand gentleman like Julius Cæsar could 'a conquered half Europe with such material. Give him viking followers and he'd 'a set the whole world spinning faster. He'd 'a managed the Britons all right then.

"He couldn't beat 'em this time. Had to go back to Rome later for a better outfit. Even then the Romans'd never have stayed in Britain for five hundred years except for a reason and a good 'un. Long before they pulled away from Britain they'd had to build forts and fortresses to keep out the man with the arrow. Not the so-called Picts and Scots—they were nothing but little harrying fellers hiding on the border. *'Twas the men behind 'em.* The man with the bow!

"Aye, the reason it was worth while for a proud nation like Rome to stay so long in Britain was nothing more nor less than to keep the arrow men from penetrating to Rome itself. *They* knew they were destined to be irresistible as Attila.

"The bow. . . . As a utility weapon it beats a six-shooter. And look what it does for the physique—that overhead pull of a weighty bow takes a man to negotiate.

"Ash. . . . Knotty ash was the best. Willow's good too if properly seasoned. Some swear by the yew, but you must not only season it a lot, you'll have to keep it in the chimney to anneal.

"Aye, after all their generations of practice with the bell, the vikings had the strongest right arm in Europe. Take the clapper out and weight the wrist in youth. But tie up the wrist first in eelskin to strengthen it.

"All his thought was for his weapon. . . . Wearing the bowstring every day, sleeping or waking, naturally keeps the enemy in mind. Wearing your jerkin on top of it. . . .

"For bowstring you must go to the British wildcat. Next best is the badger. . . .

"For feathers you'll find the goose has more fat in his feathers than any other bird. Resistant of weather. Formed by nature to brave the cold elements of the north.

"Aye the wild goose was the vikings' friend. One o' nature's roamers, navigating the sky from north to south, same as the ocean eagle draws a line from east to west.

"And death'll not always end the flight o' the wild goose. He's got a chance of taking his last flight winging an arrow from the yards. . . .

"Excuse me keeping you so long. There're times when the Golden City seems nothing more than a myth."

CHAPTER X

WEBBED HARROLD the skipper and the navigator now formed their plans. They would first search for the fleet which most likely they would find not far from Ceasars camp on the french coast if they had not already had luck. And if they failed to find them they would return home to the faroes as they had been lucky and had already secured enough easy picking to satisfy anybody, in fact their whole trip had been a great success and a voyage of pleasure. As they conversed the time flew by and the sun was setting behind a cloud which augred changeable or stormy wheather, which they both agreed was just what they wanted for their home journey, their conversation was broken off suddenly by a cry from the crows nest sail ohoi. Where away? Bearing North East. A vyking boat, looks like one of our ships. Both young Harrold and the navigator hastily ran up the rigging to the crows nest, and sure enough they saw a Norseman not square rigged like a Dane but rakey masts and flying jibs, surely either a ship from the Faroes or the south coast of Iceland or from the Fyords of Norway. As the shades of night were falling she was soon out of sight. They decided to follow her. They soon heard the Thud of the Surf beating on a flat shore and after sailing a distance they could see the fosforescent green and silver light thrown from the sea by side-jumping porpoises and other large fish and sailing on they were soon amongst the beautiful changing light made by the scudding shoals of these denisons of the Deep and these shoals always left a curling tail of varigated light behind them. This was a sure sign that they were as near the shore as they could venture as fish like men are guided by sounds, and the surfs always warned them off in time. They continued sailing with sails half Reefed, and the sounds of the surfs died away, so they concluded they had come to a river mouth or bay, and after a little while looking under the mist they saw what looked like a rock, but on watching closely they saw it was something afloat so rowing gently with muffled oars They hailed the boat by blowing on a sea horn, the answer came back by sounds from a horn who are you and having answered in a low key they were invited to come alongside. They were lucky, Harrold had found his fathers ship, but so eager were the boys to be on deck they leaped on board and were caught by the legs in the trap net which had been suspended on both sides of the deck in case of attack.* This boyish act was followed by loud laughing from both the Captured lads and the watch. Old Roger the Chief was the first to tumble from his bear skin bunk and a lanthorn was shown on the intruders, and now loud laughter at the sight brought the rest of the crew out. The nets were lowered and the lads were warmly greeted by their fathers and kin folk. And now all sat

* Mr Horn has either forgotten his original idea of an attack on Chief Roger's ship by the boys or has thought it best to moderate the incident. (Ed.)

down whilst the boys told out the interesting storey which was eagerly listened to by the Old Vykings. After this the Copper tin and Gold bars were brought from the Walruss together with jars of wine and other fine specimens of their loot. Roger now ordered Old Dick Armstrong to send up a fire-arrow warning all the forty vessels to prepare for action ready for the morrow. Armstrong made ready the arrow at once and as he was the heftiest old archer in the Faroes he was eagerly watched. He quickly pointed the bow skyward and using all his strength he shot the arrow and let go the mistle which quickly soared up and up through space while his comrades marveled. Now it gently arched over and fell seaward leaving a red fireball behind it and was easily seen by the whole fleet. The captains of the ships now hastened to their Chief and were soon engaged with plans for the attack on Seasors convoys or Ceasar himself if necessary. The day dawned and disclosed a most peculiar and picturesque sunrise a blood red sun crossed by a bar of cabalt and green showed streaky bars of fire-tipped purple topped by a fleece of blacklead and silver cloud westward and above this was a hunters moon in D barred by a thin dark line which resembled a drawn bow with arrow ready to shoot. Bill Wiseman was now ordered to spell its meaning, and all listened attentively, the red sun and green bars meant a change of wind by the time the sun was four hands high as the arrow in the hunters moon showed from the west. Wisemans predictions were hailed with delight, as this was the weather they liked best for sea fighting, whilst the big roman war galleys with their double banks of oars would be hard set in the cross seas which would be sure to be made by the change of the wind from east to west so suddenly. The Captains having arranged for their attack on the roman ships now hastily weighed anchor, and the fleet of forty moved off towards the coast of France where Ceasars supply camp was located. The wind freshened so much that by the time they turned southward towards the Channel they encountered heavy swells and cross seas which greatly helped them in their short tacks they were making with their ships devided in two lines ready for attack. They were soon in sight of a number of sail, which proved to be a convoy of six galleys heavily laden whilst 4 large war galleys were seen two on each side of the convoys for their protection. The sea Horns now sounded the Attack and the two lines moved quickly towards the first two fighting galleys, and sailing swiftly passed the two galleys which were making little headway in the cross seas. At the same time they delivered a deadly shower of arrows on the Romans who were helpless to reply. The vykings were not slow to see that they had an easy victory in sight and now they formed two circles each circling the ill-fated war galleys which rocked heavily in the cross seas and so great was the slaughter they inflicted that the poor Romans seeing their case was helpless against such a foe called for parley. The Norsmen answered Fight first and talk afterwards. But if, they said, the Romans laid down their arms they would take what loot they wanted and sail away. They wanted loot only and the quicker they got it the better. To this the Romans quickly consented. The Norse ships now ceased firing and boarding the galleys soon had the Cargoes stowed away on their vessels. The galley slaves especially gave a willing hand and helped the vyking in the work of plunder. The Romans had suffered heavily most of their Officers had fallen whilst the crew and soldiers who could do nothing to help themselves against the showers of arrows, had died at their posts. The sea robbers were highly elated at such eaisy picking and marvelled at the wealth of their catch which embraced all the skill of the Eastern world. And they left Ceasars war galleys wishing the romans better luck and a speedy return. The convoys were then attended to. They had seen the surrender of their defenders and readily assisted the sea wolves to load up. And now the Vyking being more than contended with their rich haul, left the Roman ships and Sailed away towards the Faroes with the best loot ever made in their momentous history. On their homeward trip they were greatly helped by the winds from the south west which somewhat abated as they neared their homeland. As they came in sight of their Island Keeps they were joined by the gulls from Faroes. Many of these were known to the Norsemen. Two of these especially one they called grey cap had grown to a tremendous size and was well known as also was another large bird which had a twisted bill and this one they called Cissor Bill. These birds were generally on the Out Look for their returning boats and many of them came with their young breed to meet the home comers. As they neared their home shore they were eagerly greeted by their folks and when they had Cast Anchor and landed a loud pandemonium took place. The truants especially were joyfully received by their anxious mothers. Days were spent in dividing the spoils which were so various and valuable that it made the Vykings of the Faroes the richest people in the Western world. And all preyed that Seasar who had brought them such Wealth and handed it over so easily would live long and come often.

FINIS

CONVERSATION

"Well, ma'am, I've come to the finis this week. 'Twas a bit noisy yesterday for polishing your thoughts, but that caretaker let me use his room for quietness' sake. Sort of office with his bed in it, where he can see who comes up the stairs. Not too good as a study but the excursions of the mind are apt to enlarge any spot *kismet* brings you to.

"A good table there too. However that may be you'll see I was able to conjure up ten Roman galleys and Roger's forty sail into the office, so called. Quite a little armada!

"Taking provisions to Cæsar, those six galleys. And four big war galleys for protection. Some good Italian light wines and all the rich viands of a luxurious race. Silken cushions and expensive furs for the winter in Britain. Heavy woollen togas'd be dyed crimson or blue for the looks of it. Leather capes and buskins to keep the snow out.

"Aye, when Imperator Romanus hears what's happened to his provisions he'll experience a bad quarter of an hour. Grieving over the wine and so on. 'These webbed foots are surely choicey,' he'll say when he sees all the best wine gone. It naturally hastens his return to Rome for reinforcements.

"Aye, there's a bit of a snap in battle writing! I could 'a drawn it out for several pages but there'd be no gain in the ultimate. You may multiply the arrows and increase the flow of blood but you'll not make a deeper impression on the reader. I could 'a made a bloody panorama out o' those galley slaves seizing their advantage. You don't suppose their first thought was for the wine jars. Their first duty'd be towards that feller with the whip always on their bare backs. There'd be screams rending the air . . . a rat smothered with the dogs. . . .

"But it doesn't do to let yourself go. Commonising the book, and so on. Better throw the spotlight on the wine jars than on a spectacle of human agony. Conviviality'll always take better in the ultimate than a surfeit of violence.

"Sea fighting's surely a finer spectacle than what the army'll ever provide. More dignity to it, plus somewhat less of the horrors. No dying horses to make humanity ashamed. Poor young fellers being tempted to run, et cetra. It's a man to man affair on the sea and be done with it. And the grand action of the ships . . .

viking or Roman, a ship battling out for its life on heaving waters is a spectacle for gods.

"Aye, if anything'll reconcile the Great Onlooker to the sins of humanity it's the ships and the sailors. They'll always take a sporting chance. . . .

"The best and cheapest way of sinking an enemy's ship was to employ the round robin, and at the same time to send one of your heavy oak ships full speed past the Romans' galley—just near enough to sweep every oar. Smashes 'em. No need to go round and repeat the dose on the other side—they'll be awkward enough with one side incapacitated. But if another set is put out you'll have to do that too. In the mean time the fellers with the arrows are doing their duty in the yards. Aye. . . . And what with the oaken dragon smashing your oars and the deadly doings of arrows shot from a heavy bow by the world's bowmen, plus the drawback of not having been trained to keep your stomach down in a heavy sea—if you were anything but a gallant Roman you'd go below and say your prayers to whatever gods you fancy at the moment.

"A gallant gentleman, Julius Cæsar. To state the fact that he'd never turn a hair when at arrow distance is not to belittle the arrow as a weapon but to belaud the valour of the man Julius.

"The vikings were surely sports. That's why they always talked about Julius Cæsar with respect. The whole consensus of the meaning of a man in Lancashire is a sport like Julius Cæsar. A far higher feller than Brutus and immune to women. His nature was too cold for friendship. . . .

"Et tu quoque, Brute. . . .

"Aye, it knocked the spirit out of him when he saw his friend against him. Finished he was, at that lamentable sight.

"You can diagnose some men and find they can't even be the friends of themselves. A deceitful friend is no more your enemy than his own.

"Buntlings, gaffs, and everything they had. . . .

"A spinning-jenny on each side. . . . Ma'am? Well, that's a sea term I'm telling you for the tactics of the bowmen circling round a big ship they're firing at. A boomerang movement, same as the spinning-jennys we used to throw in the air when we were lads.

"Ma'am? No, that's only a bit o' machinery you're talking about, excuse me. Arkwright's idea. Nothing but a barber, but being Lancashire he battled out after an idea. What I'm discussing is the boomerang action of the bowmen in sea warfare. Same as the sycamore seeds we'd throw up when we were lads. . . . A proper little scientific notion o' nature's, that sycamore seed.

"Seeds. . . . You'll not discern much difference between God and nature when you've watched all the clever botanical tricks in Equatorial Africa. Survival of the species. . . . You'll believe that nice little notion about the farthing sparrow that's in the Bible when you see the ingenuities of nature not to lose a species if she can humanly help it. There's big science at the back of her notions *re* transport of seeds. . . .

"Naturally what's got to be considered is the easiest boarding of a ship that's protected with bristling oars.

"Well, of course if it's a viking ship it can only be boarded at the helm, unless you've made up your mind to splinter the oars. And that's not so easy when there's two banks of 'em. Here, on the top—if you'll lend me your pencil a moment, I'll show you—here on the top are the sweeps. The great top oars that'd need two to four men at each. The blades of 'em reach far out across the water. A fine sweep they make that's like a half moon in shape. And below the sweeps there'll be the shorter oars playing their own stroke below. You see the shape of it's like a bowstring and a bow. And naturally maintaining a different rhythm. Nothing different from a smaller tune you'll hear going on beside a big one in these so-called choruses. *Hallelujah Chorus* and so on that they play on the brass bands in Lancashire . . .

"Aye, Lancashire. Tommy Bamber had ancient knowledge of sea fighting. Me Greatuncle Horn used to send for him to talk about the earlies. When you're blind you've got to find people can amuse you. Tommy Bamber'd been at Galveston. Had inner knowledge of the *Alabama* too.

"Dressed his hair like an old-time sailor, Tommy Bamber. The longest whiskers in Lancashire and wore his hair netted. The flashings stuck out at the side—turned under and bobbed at the end and they'd put wire or whalebone inside for protection against wounds in a fight. Whalebone's very handy to resist the sword and the club and other weapons. Done into a bowline knot —every loop tied with a bowline knot.

"Nothing prettier than a bowline knot in hair. If you saw it done in the cinema you'd sure get some o' these street women copying it for the looks of it. It'd surely be dandy in a cinema. . . .

"And buckskin breeches. . . . Old English buckskin, soft as silk, and a wooden leg.

"Ma'am? Well, certainly. I may not have mentioned it before, but with so much on my mind as I have at my age, and after all the little expeditions I've had, it's surely an easy thing to forget a wooden leg. Tommy Bamber's leg was no more than a bit of nature to us. We forget to notice he wasn't in full possession of his faculties.

"Aye, my Greatuncle Horn'd often send for him. Knew each other's ways, and so on. Look at those trees he would have cut down. Nothing'd please him but they must come down, family or no family. Greatuncle Horn always had his way against the family, ninety or no ninety. Wanted to cut down a row of fine withies in the garden. Nice trees, but the drops of dew used to fall on his bald head when he went for his walk every morning early. Being a blind man it naturally made him jump more than if he'd had all his vision.

"Tap-tapping with his stick there every morning. . . . Always under that row of trees. . . . Bald on top, but he had a good fringe of locks—fell all round to his shoulders, old style. His dress was old style too, close breeches and a buckle on his shoes. Too much of a gentleman of fortune ever to deck his limbs in these trousers they've worn so long. An effeminate style, hiding the calf and the set of a man's knee as much as a lady's fancy crinoline.

"Aye, if the reign of Albert the Good hadn't been quite so prolonged there's no knowing whether trousers would have gone on for so many generations. Hiding what was meant by nature to be seen.

"Ma'am? Why, certainly he did. Those trees came down. Naturally he'd all the family like a nest of hornets about his ears. Vandalism and so on they said. Couldn't he change his beat, they said. Look at the beauty of them! they said.

"But that's just what he couldn't do, although I've seen him pass his hand over the bark of a tree. Feeling the pattern of it and so on. Following the shape of a leaf with his fingers. And you'd see his nostrils up in the wind like a dog, getting the aroma of what he'd see no more. . . . The ploughing and what not and the hawthorn in its season. . . .

"Aye, but he wasn't listening to the family. Sent a private messenger to Tommy Bamber to come and cut the trees. Understanding his nature, Tommy Bamber came at once—quick as a man could that's not got his due number of legs. 'Twasn't long before me Great-uncle Horn was taking his walks again there. The same path that was familiar to his stick but no drops on his head.

"Ma'am? Why, no—he'd never have worn a hat in the garden. Never been used to it.

"Greatuncle Horn was in good humour until he died. Always had his own way, that was it.

"Aye, it was surely better to die having his own way than to be put fretful to bed with death and the family peeping round the curtains. He surely gave the Great Leveller somewhat of a surprise when he fell off the hay-load that time. Enough to give the old man a bit of a chuckle when he woke up in the next world.

"Aye, death never tied him to his bed to be stared at by a set of relations, all with their mourning handkerchiefs at attention.

"Come to that, what was me Greatuncle Horn but a violent buccaneer in the vitals? When the sea's been calling out for centuries there's always some in a family can't refuse it. A prospector must follow the gold, and gold is what the sea always held for the old Horns.

"The ships changed a bit in shape, I'll not deny. But there's not so much difference between that old viking apparition with the dragon on it and the old slavers as you might fancy. Change your trident for a cutlass—the blood on it's the same. 'Tis when you see the changes of the last hundred years. . . . From a slaver to one of these modern get-ups. Lavatories and wireless, the barber's scent shop and not a stitch o' good sail or a bit of a brass cannon. Nothing left for a man like my greatuncle, no pride left. Nothing but the imaginary enjoyment of sending out peculiar vessels for South American wars'd make Lancashire smile. All bombast, these so-called revolutions. Fancy uniforms for excitable little fellers.

"Aye, me Greatuncle Horn . . .

"If I could tell him about some o' my river fights he'd laugh himself out of his grave. 'Twould surely have brought a little pleasure into his life in the hereafter to know how I used the half-moon formation for my savage canoes and find it work, same as it worked in the dawn of history with the webfoots and their ships of oak. . . .

"Me father was a wild un too. A forty-niner. Lucky Jack he was called out there. California. Found a great nugget shaped like a bullfrog that's been famous in its time.

"Aye, he was always one that fancied roaming. But it got on his mind in the ultimate. Wanted to expiate his wanderings in the next generation. Me two brothers were trained for priests. He destined me too for something respectable. 'Twould a' satisfied his conscience to see me settled down. 'Settled down?' I said to him. 'You've bred me and you've bred me wild. Now you talk of settling down. 'Tis yourself opened the cage before I was born, and you'll not keep me in it now,' I said to him. Poor feller, he was a good parent. He sighed a bit and said: 'Come and have a drink, lad.' We were more like brothers after that. There's good in every man, only know where to tap it. Aye. . . . 'There's sights and visions,' I said, 'far beyond what I can get here and I mean to seize 'em.'

"Aye, and I could a' seen more if I hadn't tied myself up in wedlock to a ringletted Lancashire lass. Same as I used to have in mind when I was a lad learning ivory. Wasted several years trying to settle down. Scotland Yard and so on.

"Marriage is not what it used to be. In the old days 'twas carefully thought out to increase the importance of your tribe. But in these days a matter of chance'll cut off your roving days for good if you're not careful.

"The old viking was a masterpiece at making alliances. Held himself aloof—his language'll show it, broad Lancashire—but was always ambitious to spread his race on other shores. 'My brother from Norway.' 'My cousin from Ireland.' That's what it was with them. Plant some of your roots in a neighbouring country and you've always got sanctuary.

"Well, a man needs a getaway. That's why England chased after the colonies. She learnt the habit from the vikings, but it's not the same now as those natural marriage alliances. There's no international fancy relationship, whatever this so-called League of Nations may say, that's ever come up to marriage—the great leveller, so styled.

"Aye, I wasted several years for respectability's sake. Scotland Yard and so on for a living I could 'a made easier and with less trouble out in the open somewhere.

"There's some women you could drag about like the French drag their so-called *maitresses* when they're developing a colony. But there's not many you'd care to have hampering your freedom. No getaway where there's a woman. The French'll never extend their colonies the width of a bean row.

"Aye, London was panorama enough for a time but hardly suitable for a feller likes change. If it hadn't 'a been for George Bussey being friendly to young fellers, Evans' Cowyard and so on, there were no spotlights in the metropolis to make me stay there.

"There was brains at Evans' Cowyard. Agreeable conversation with fellers'd never be *Homo stultus*. That feller Phil May I've told you about—liked to draw the coster families and made a handsome living out of it for a few days at a time. . . . He'd come running in and crying out for a dickey. 'Get me a dickey, for God's sake, some one! . . .' A feller that couldn't support a shirt'd have to wear a dickey for respectability's sake.

"Aye, he'd have a good clean up at Evans' Cowyard and he'd go out and make a few hundred pounds. 'A penn'orth o' gin and a polly.' [?] That was a sketch brought him in quite a lot. When he was half-slewed May'd make money faster than what most of us could do in a mood of sobriety.

"That crush'd sure got brains. Famous resort for poets and everything else.

"Brain's always an incentive, poet or painter. George Bussey. . . . He knew a lot o' fellers like that. Used to meet in the old Portugal in the Strand. A number of aristocracy amongst them. George made quite a bit of a living finishing up before he became Master of Hansard.

"Ma'am? Well, I mean fellers that had notions minus the industrial power'd go to George. There was a crazy writer—name's gone from me—used to go to the Fox and Grapes. . . .

"The old Fox Under the Hill. Bussey used to go there. A nice place, Dulwich. Doctor Johnson, Boswell and other literates used to go there for relaxation from London life. A regular *posse* of them, engineered by Johnson, the friend o' Goldsmith. . . . The poor feller that travelled in the Carpathians playing a tin whistle. A proper tramp. . . .

"Aye, that feller turned his face to nature at an era when Johnson could think of nothing but walking the streets of London plotting out words for a dictionary. Dictionary? *Ikona!* There's no words needed in a state of nature. 'Tis nature supplies his ideas to a poet. Poor Noll got more majesty from nature than he ever could seize for himself from an expensive dictionary. 'Tis an idea you're needing first. When you've chased that along then the words'll come up from a natural spring. *Ikona*—dictionary. . . .

" 'Princes and powers they flush and fade away——'

"Listen to the sweet fancy sound of it. A proper panorama of a sunset.

"There was a village he knew called . . . called. . . .

"He used to write about it. It's escaped me for the moment but it'll be there in the morning if I think about it before I fall asleep.

"Ma'am? . . . Aye—*Auburn!* You knew it then!

" 'Sweet Auburn, loveliest village of the plain——'

"That's it! I just wanted me cue. When you get to

my age you will always be searching back for a cue to your thoughts.

"Auburn. . . . A peaceful spot, would create nostalgia in any world roamer. A parson in it doing his duty to all and sundry. 'Passing rich on forty pounds a year,' it says. 'Twas more than poor Noll got for his pretty idea of a village. But a feller like that, that's gifted with the poet's eye, gets his meat and drink from the heart. All the coin he's paid with he'll never see.

"Aye, immortality's still being paid out to a man can't feel the coin on his palm. Played for his supper on a tin whistle. Had to seize his food same as me, at the dictates of hunger. . . .

"Ma'am? Oh, *that* feller . . . his name's gone from me but he used to go to the Fox and Grapes. Never could finish his books off. Leave his ideas all in a snarl, like a kitten that's tired of a ball of wool. But George'd make it right for fellers of that sort.

"Then there were Parliamentarians George had to lend a hand to. Noble lords and so on'd take a skeleton speech and say 'George, how'll this frame?' And George'd take it home and fill it up and read it to his wife and send it back to the lord. Naturally 'twas easy to slip in a bit of good stuff of his own without the feller suspecting it—a Parliamentarian's always apt to overestimate his capacities. Exaggeration's always been the *summa cacumna* [?] of his ambitions.

"Aye, if all things were known, there's not many men've done as much for their country as George Bussey. On the top of Hansard he made a fancy sort of a living guiding the eloquence of the aristocracy. Young fellers from Oxford'd be inclined to overdo it. They'd have to be advised to lay low in their panegyrics. The fact was—these young fellers—if they belonged to anything in golden crinolines and fully coronetted, sitting up there in the gallery, 'twas easy to bring down the House with a few fancy notions.

"Ladies watching their sons set sail in the ocean of politics. . . . There's many an anxious mother been to George. Anxious about the hecklers and so forth. It's surely a mystery to any loving mother that any soul should contradict her child. In public too. Aye, women have always kept their hand on politics. 'Tis the ambitious ones've never asked for the vote. They don't need it. Exercising the privileges of womanhood and so forth, there's no occasion for it.

"What these young fellers failed to realise was that it's not making a speech gets you along. It's the defence you put up against interrupters. For interrupters there's nobody in the world so suitable as a very highly educated individual. Bit o' Latin and so on. Quotations from the classics or Shakespeare can be disconcerting in public. Especially to a young Oxford lad's had nothing but too much desk and debating societies and so forth—a professional interrupter'll knock him over like a ninepin.

"Oxford. . . . We did a bit round Oxford one time, me and a partner I had.

"Well—topical we were doing. A song and a bit of a caper or two'd always go down with young fellers at the seat of learning. In those days a guitar plus a bit of sentiment'd always hit the young. Always fetch more than a common hurdy-gurdy or other mechanism.

"There's something in strings. . . . Look at my Pangues! You think you've got a savage to deal with. But when you hear the harps on running water and the grand humming of deep voices you're being instructed that there's something comes between man and darkest savagedom, and that's rhythm. Aye, 'tis rhythm raises him. Same as it's rhythm turns a man into a soldier before he knows it. Talk of hypnotism—nothing but a fancy name for rhythm.

"Aye, when I used to be in one of these newspaper offices . . . I could turn a good laughable article at one time. Papers like the *Rocky Mountain Observer,* and so on, where you can cover ignorance by wit. 'Can you write a rural article?' they'd say. 'Why, sure.' And all you've got to do is to sidetrack the reader from the farmyard and the crops to something more humorous and it'll go down and more be asked for. To be able to joke about a turnip makes for popularity somewhat sooner than a knowledge of botany, profound though it may be.

"Aye, but twisting up the news to a palatable form for *Homo stultus* is no outlook for the ambitious. Sitting in an office over there, I couldn't see a feller strolling along easy with a banjo but I had to be out and after him. To get over the horizon's always been ambition enough for me. Aye, there's something in strings, plucked out o' doors, that's like wine to the roamer. He forgets the sorrows of work and laughs to be alive.

"Newspapers. . . . Something unnatural about staying in one spot to gather up all the facts of the universe. If you want facts you must travel for 'em. You pick things up as a wanderer you'd never learn by living there. Aye, you get both sides of the medal then. Same as when you're in the States you learn history by going from North to South. Got to hear both sides before you can balance it up. Texas and so on. I wandered about a good deal there. Could always earn a dollar or two and a meal by making a picture or painting a sign.

"Art in Texas is at the lowest ebb. They'll give their hearts for a picture there. I taught the rudiments of painting to the daughters of A—— and B——. Wealthy fellers, those, but pitiful in their ignorance. Hungry to see the children do what life has denied to themselves. Piano, oil painting, et cetra and so forth. Elocution, so called.

"Aye, putting up a fine statue to Bill Austin'll not paint the common ignorance out o' the man. 'Tis better to educate the children of a freebooter than to try and whitewash the feller personally. A statue of the dead never brought any progress to any country. 'Tis the living've got to be sculpted into shape.

"But roaming blood's hard to stem; oils, the classics, or whatever's poured into you at school. Me father was a wild 'un too. Lucky Jack, but he'd let luck slip through his fingers like a lord. . . .

"Well, in those shipping families—mercantile marines, I'd call 'em—there's always one to go wild. If it hadn't been me it might a' been my sister. Not the one that's a spinster at home but the one that's a sister of charity. Aye, she might a' been a vagrant woman if she hadn't become a nun to ease her emotions. 'Tis the wild 'uns not the meek ones'll seek discipline. Same as an animal craves salt.

"Next to me, that one. . . . A sweet voice she had. *Ave Maria,* and so on . . .

"Well, ma'am, I'm outstaying me allotted welcome somewhat to-day. I've got the lads safe home to the Faroes all right. You could always touch it up a little where it's needful. Dwell a bit longer on the home-coming of the truants. That's a bit of topical'll always move the heart. Anxious mothers, and so on. Shading their eyes for a sail. . . .

"But come to anxiety as such, the viking woman was better off than most. Having no newspapers or telegrams to worry her with the truth she could always picture the best till the last minute. Top o' that, it was the viking's idea never to tell news of battle or impending warfare to his woman. She was never told anything. Knowledge for ladies was reckoned a drawback. There must be no fear to belittle the prowess of the unborn and the little children.

"Aye, a good laugh when danger was over and plenty o' bright loot tumbled out on the beach—that was her share of responsibility beyond what she carried as a homekeeper. 'Long as she never neglected to wear the bowstring she was not asked to express any tactics in the affairs of state. But she'd be a bold woman all the same, even if silent. The viking had to choose his mate for prowess in the family, not for fancy ringlets and a rosebud skin. The mother's half holds, they say in Lancashire.

"Aye, the vikings had to look for their existence to bodily prowess, whether inherited from the mother or the father. The brains of a clark'd never a' done *them* any good. What's the good of a shield when there's no man behind it?

"I could 'a put in a good deal of laughter and merriment for the return of the boats, *They* never needed a jester. Never any need of jesters where there's Lancashire women. Fine, laughing women . . . Of course they kept a few beauclarks. Sages, so called. But that's business, not pleasure. Wisdom you may say. It's only the Latins that needed to be made to laugh by a paid slave. The Franks and so on caught the trick o' forced laughter.

"Laughter enough without any jester in a good ship spinning through surf homeward bound. And when they got home they'd not want to be amused. They'd sit quiet by the fire, telling the children and so on, and listening to the wife give her complaints. And the harpers'd regale them with songs of history, but it wasn't to create a laugh. A common notion, always to be seeking laughter.

"A crude lot, the viking ladies! Couldn't write a ream. And being densely innocent of knowledge, the only fun they had came out o' the sea.

"Aye, the clam and shell folk o' Lancashire—they still find laughter on the seashore.

"Rights o' foreshore, rights o' piracy and a fifth to the Queen. 'Twas something bigger than clam gathering when that girl Elizabeth was Virgin Queen. It's a known fact that she got so much riches from the Americans that she lost her head. Performed an orgy of extravagance after the defeat of Spain. Got some lover to build her an expensive Elizabethan mansion at Richmond. Mulled ale flowing free in the streets o' Richmond while the building was going on. Mechanics drinking mulled ale on the Spaniards' money while the queen and her paramour laughed at the window. . . .

"It was then she created the fief. Reverted to viking law on the strength of knocking out the Armada. A fifth to the Queen—that's what the Horns always owed for any piracies natural to their strip of the coast.

"A proper pirate, that girl. When the Armada was getting near she went clean off her head at the idea of the church stuff all glistening with jewels they'd be able to seize off the galleons when they came careening too near the coast. It's well known in history that she'd a' given even her one pair of silk stockings for the sight of a bit of loot.

"Aye, when a woman turns pirate there's no guiding her. The female of the species is more deadly than the male. And that's where Shakespeare showed the wisdom he'd snatched from the confessional. Her noble father, Henry, amused himself knocking the Virgins out o' their niches in the Reformation, but Elizabeth's eye roamed further. That girl saw the whole world as a playground for Protestants and piracy. This so-called Protestant religion has always been a suitable creed to hang over the Jolly Roger. What can you expect when there's no confession and you're born an islander. . . .

"Well, naturally those rich galleons were never right for an attack on a Protestant country. When the British saw how dead easy it was to handle the Spanish that'd been the terror of Europe, they laughed. 'Twas the first lesson they learnt about the hollowness of the Latin races. Elizabeth was mightily amused to have captured a cardinal, she and a lot of barbarous ladies like herself. They were only great girls and it sure tickled them. But you'll not forget when Britain's at stake the Catholics are up in arms quick as the Protestant, although never mixing.

"Sometimes a Catholic's obliged to put country first, same as we did when the Spaniards cast an eye over England and called it religion. Aye, but to entertain Spain on English soil was a very different thing from entertaining Rome in the four walls of a church. Despite the teachings of religion England's one when it comes to keeping out the Latins.

"Lancashire and Yorkshire can forget their ancient feuds and furores when they see a feller like Philip approaching in his galleons. A bombastic vessel, a galleon. Built on a keel all wrong for swiftness. . . .

"The mistake from the beginning was the notion of

setting Spain against Lancashire. The dagoes never had a chance against the vikings. 'Twas Lancashire tactics sunk the Armada.

"Aye, Lancashire. . . .

"And there's another thing you can give Lancashire credit for, and that's Domesday Book. When it was a disgrace to be able to write you'd see the seal smitten by the fist of the great chiefs. 'My hand and seal and good enough for a gentleman'. Aye, they needed no learned spelling when it came to recording English soil for the benefice of the generations. The sign of the fist will always supersede the pen, come to holding England against the world.

"Lancashire and Yorkshire'll never let go of her chiefs. Look at Howard o' Glossop, paramount chief of the English! Hereditary King. No Hanover'll ever be King there. Call 'em duke as a sop. But if it's *King,* Lancashire doffs to her hereditary chieftains and nothing less.

"Look at Victoria with her whimsied fancies! She must go to Lancashire and display herself. But Disraeli hurried her through. They hissed her at Preston and it made him nervous. She began to weep about it and he said 'You may lose your head and crown, young lady, if you go any further.' 'Twas the first time she shed a tear for political reasons. Aye. . . . But he had a master's way with women, and he said 'If you'll dry your tears, my girl, and trust to me, I'll make you an Empress before we've done.' So they got back to London. Back to cockneydom. . . .

"Aye, Lancashire's always been a natural fortress of hereditary power. Yorkshire the same, come to business. They've got a paramount, same as we have. Lancashire and Yorkshire may have had their family quarrels in the time of the Roses. But in face of a common enemy they agree to sink that. A gamecock recognises another gamecock. And if one o' them crows some day, *don't you think he will be answered? Aye?*

"Well, ma'am—we've come to a tangent in literary affairs. If it's finis I'm quite prepared to look the word in the face, same as a rogue elephant's got to, soon or late. Don't agitate yourself to spare my feelings. Writing a story for lads has surely been an agreeable interlude. Barter's a meagre diet for old age to finish on. More dignity in literature.

"If only some lads'd read this narrative o' mine. . . . It might tickle lads. They understand runaways, same as I do. When you've been one yourself. . . .

"Aye, it's been a bit of all sorts, but a story's got to have some come from. I've always liked history that nobody knows. Although, mind you, Lingard's as good a guide as any, if you must have one. The feller that starts to weave out a historical narrative without standing fair on his facts is apt to find himself on *pons asinorum*. I've read some of these writing fellers' attempts when I was a lad at school. But they can't cut a viking. Too much playacting and costumery. You want a feller bred to the job to make 'em live natural.

"Excuse me mentioning it, but I've woven you in a little description of signals in battle I thought'd be useful. Look pleasing in a cinema. A sort of mirage, and the fire arrow soaring over the fleet o' dragonships. . . . All eyes following it. . . .

"Conches *and* arrow signs they used. A proper system. The old *concha* could tell tidings to a fine shade. Aye, the old sea-horn's told many a piercing tale across the spume. It sure was the wild voice of battle. . . .

"Ma'am? Well, I've explained to you—the chief'd use red or green arrows for tidings. On the starboard side, naturally, and running from ship to ship like a voice o' fire.

"Those were the days of men. 'Twas risk bred 'em. Sea risk and battle risk. . . . A proper spawn of the foam—webfoots. . . .

"Ma'am? Well, naturally the red arrow meant war. Green arrow means peace, same as throwing salt on the fire. . . .

"Well, I mean on the war fires, what else? You've forgotten, excuse me being a bit sharp. . . . So that those far away could see the colour of it when it flamed up green. Aye. . . .

"Ma'am? Well, of course, they put tinder on the fire arrow. Touchwood, I told you, and sulphur. Dug in the north o' Scotland. . . . And as the arrow soars it'll fall off in a fiery red ball. Red for war, as has always been from the dawn of history. And green for peace. . . .

" 'Tis what we listened to when we were lads by the fire at Frea. We'd sleep with our bowstrings about us, too, after listening to Tommy Bamber's talk.

" 'Tis only what he got from his grandfather. He'd take a drink and start another. Story or ballad, 'twas all the same to him. We lads'd be seeing boggarts across the snow—glad to be near each other for company's sake. . . .

> 'Lord Lovel he kissed his fair young bride,
> She said "Tarry a minute, I'll hide, I'll hide!" '——

My voice is somewhat thin to-day. . . .

"Always a strong winter when I was a lad. . . .

"Aye, Lancashire makes a good hearth. 'Tis the old armoury of England where the fighting wits are kept. . . .

"Lancashire makes a good hearth. Come to that, what's a hearth without a roamer? . . . Somebody to open the door that's not been expected? . . .

"Why, what would Lancashire think if she lost all her roamers? A mother always loves the wild 'uns best. She wants life in the house, and that's what he brings her from the strange panoramas he's seen. Same as my viking lads took the gewgaws and scented pomades of Rome to their mothers. Make 'em laugh a bit and they'll not be too angry with the wild 'uns.

"If only some lads will read my notions. Lads and their fathers. . . .

THE END